BEES and BEE-KEEPING

BEES and
BEE-KEEPING

MARIA COSTANTINO

© 2011 Kerswell Farm Ltd

This edition published by King Books

Printed 2011

This book is distributed in the UK by
Parkham Books Ltd
Barns Farm, Boraston
Tenbury Wells
Worcestershire
WR15 8NB

david@kingbooks.co.uk

ISBN: 978-1-906239-84-8

DS0237. Bees and Beekeeping

Creative Director: Sarah King
Project editor: Sally MacEachern
Designer: Jade Sienkiewicz

Printed in China

1 3 5 7 9 10 8 6 4 2

Contents

Keeping Bees

INTRODUCTION

How doth the little busy bee
Improve each shining hour,
And gather honey all the day
From every opening flower!

(Isaac Watts, *Divine Songs for Children*, 1715)

It is estimated that around 70 per cent of all the food we eat is dependent on pollination by bees and other insects. Albert Einstein calculated that, without bees, mankind would only survive for four years. But as well as being important in the maintenance of the planet's ecosystem, bees also produce a magnificent foodstuff that humans have been eating for thousands of years: honey.

Honey is one of nature's wonder products. Naturally sweeter than sugar, one cup of honey weighs about 340 g (12 oz), while a cup of sugar weighs around 200 g (7 oz). Honey contains an enzyme that stops it from going mouldy and, consequently, needs no preservatives. Indeed, jars of honey that were interred with the ancient Egyptians in their tombs over 3,300 years ago, when opened, were found to be as fresh tasting as they would have been if produced in a hive just one summer ago. In addition to honey, bees also provide some further wonderful products: beeswax, royal jelly and honeycomb have long been used in the home, in cooking and in medicine.

With an increasing awareness — and urgency — regarding our environmental responsibilities, keeping bees is one way in which we can make a difference. For a start, we would have a natural sweetener at our fingertips. This would allow us to cut down on air miles for imported sugar cane products or even 'mass-produced' blended honey (much of which is imported from China and South America). On the other hand, a novice with just two or three hives in the garden can provide between 20 and 100 jars of honey with a unique flavour and scent, because the honey produced in the hives is influenced by the local weather over the season and by the flowers that are growing in a 5-km (3-mile) radius of the apiary. But you don't have to live in the country to produce beautiful honey. Beehives are popping up in town and city gardens across the world. In the heart of London's West End, the Fortnum & Mason store on Piccadilly has beehives on its roof that supply the store with honey for sale and for use in its restaurants. Like many 'London bees', Fortnum's bees enjoy the many parks, flowerbeds, allotments and gardens of the city — including those of nearby Buckingham Palace.

While this book is not intended as a textbook, it does attempt to give an overview of what is involved in keeping bees so that you can make an informed decision before you start. It outlines some of the demands in terms of equipment and time that you will need to care for and manage your colony and your hives. The art and craft of bee-keeping has evolved over thousands of years. The novice's first steps in bee-keeping are best undertaken with the support and knowledge of a local bee-keeping association, the contact details for which are given at the end of this book (see page 144).

A BRIEF HISTORY OF BEE-KEEPING

Honeybees have been on earth for around 120 million years, pollinating flowers and producing honey. Prehistoric cave paintings dating from some 10,000 years ago show humans extracting honey and wax from hives. At some stage, ancient man observed that bees retreated from smoke. The honeybee's natural habitat is a hollowed-out tree, but these are prone to lightning strikes and consequent fires. So, the appearance of smoke around the hive alerted the bees to flee and seek out a new nest. Before evacuating the 'burning' hive, the bees gorged themselves on the stored honey and bees with full bellies, it was discovered, were less aggressive. This made them less likely to sting, which meant the fruits of their labour could be collected without injury.

Fortunately, mankind also saw that the bees would return to a hive after a false alarm, to recommence their work and it was a short step to the creation of simple man-made hives in order to farm bees locally. The first hives were, no doubt, close replicas of hollow trees. In parts of Africa simple log hives with the ends of the hollow log stopped up with baked clay plugs and a small side entrance providing bee access are still widely used today, as are woven baskets covered in clay.

Early domestication of bees

The successful domestication of honeybees was achieved by many ancient civilisations, and the role the bee played in agriculture, medicine and daily life in some instances became part of the religious beliefs of the cultures. The honeybee became the symbol of Upper Egypt in the 3rd Dynasty (c. 2686–2613 BCE). After the unification of Upper and Lower Egypt, the bee became the symbol of the whole kingdom, with each pharaoh bearing the throne name of 'King of Bees'.

During the 5th Dynasty (c. 2498–2345 BCE), which saw the rise of the cult of Ra at Heliopolis, the Egyptians believed that the sun god Ra dropped his tears as honeybees and that they would fall in the human realm as honey and beeswax. On the walls of the 5th Dynasty sun temple of Nyuserre Ini in Egypt, are paintings showing priests and workers blowing 'sacred' smoke into beehives and removing the honey. So highly prized was honey, that sealed pots were found among the grave goods in pharaohs' tombs, including that of Tutankhamen, and honey was traded and imported from across North Africa and from Asia.

Honeybees were also traded as far afield as Asia Minor and southern Europe, evidenced by the distribution of Egyptian strains of honeybees such as Apis lamarckii, A. saharensis and A. yementica. The ancient Israelites and Canaanites also undertook bee-keeping on a large scale. In the ruined city of Rehov, archaeologists uncovered the remains of several rows, each of 100 beehives made of unbaked clay and straw, dating from 900 BCE. Thirty of them were intact.

Bee-keeping in the Western world

Bee-keeping was later documented by the Greeks, whose gods on Mount Olympus are renowned for having feasted on ambrosia (honey) and nectar. References to bees, hives and their maintenance, as well as the culinary and medicinal benefits of honey, can be found in the writings of Hippocrates from the 4th century BCE. In Greece apiculture was not only part of religious life, but it developed into a science. Pythagoras saw the geometry of the honeycomb itself as mirroring the structure of the universe. The ordered, yet hierarchical, nature of 'bee life' influenced political thought on the nature of human society and the notions of democracy. The Greek practice of keeping bees in expandable ceramic, lidded hives, which allowed them to be kept on a semi-permanent basis, was eventually passed to the Romans who spread apiculture across the Western world as the empire expanded its borders. The Romans excelled at constructing hives, which were fabricated variously from wood, clay bricks and even dried cow dung.

Virgil, in his *Georgics*, a four-volume didactic poem written in the 1st century BCE, wrote extensively on the cultivation of the soil, the rearing of cattle and the keeping of bees. It discussed where to site hives, how to deal with swarms, gathering honey and bee diseases. Virgil also described the hive as a 'tiny republic', and for centuries afterwards, political thinkers – including Erasmus and Karl Marx – used the bee colony as a metaphor for the different forms

of society they proposed, ranging from absolute monarchy, to republicanism and socialist Utopia. The industrious nature of bees has long been used an example for humans to copy.

Just as these thinkers acknowledged that human societies required the rule of men, it was also presumed that the bee colony was also a patriarchal system and that the biggest bee in the hive was a king and not a queen. It was not until 1623 that the English bee expert Charles Butler proposed a bee matriarchy in his thesis 'The Feminine Monarchy'. It took a further century for Butler's notion to be scientifically proven by the Dutch scientist Jan Swammerdam, in his *Book of Nature*.

In the so-called Dark Ages that followed the Romans, bee-keeping continued largely unchanged. Most colonies were housed in straw skeps (see page 59). These basket-work containers were based on earlier Greek ceramic hives and continue to be used today, particularly for catching swarms. (In some countries the use of skeps for keeping bees is illegal, because the hive has to be broken open to harvest the honey and the colony is destroyed). Skeps were prone to rotting in wet climates, so bee-keepers constructed walls with holes in which to place and protect the skeps and their inhabitants. These bee boles continued to be made up to the 18th century, particularly in larger houses, where they became an important architectural feature.

With the spread of Christianity in the West, by the early Middle Ages in Europe, the Church was a dominant force in both culture and commerce, playing a large role in bee-keeping, brewing and medicine. Honey was used in the brewing of mead and was a vital ingredient in many elixirs of the time. Some, like the famous Benedictine and Chartreuse liqueurs, are still made today, their names betraying their ecclesiastical roots. As the Egyptians had done 3,000 years earlier, the Church also made use of beeswax for making candles. In England in the 12th century, candle-making became a profession practised by wax chandlers whose main customers were the Church and nobility – commoners would have used cheaper, smokier, rush lights dipped in tallow (animal fat). Today, in the City of London, there is still a Worshipful Company of Wax Chandlers.

In the 17th century, the bee became the official symbol of the Catholic papacy and, until 1900, Catholic churches were required by papal decree to burn only beeswax candles. The same wax had long been used to make stoppers for bottles and jars, for polishing woodwork and saddles, waterproofing leather, softening hard-worked hands and for making sear cloths, strips of linen dipped into melted wax and used warm by apothecaries to bind up wounds.

The modern beehive

The practice of bee-keeping continued throughout the 18th century and well into the 19th century, as honey remained the principle sweetener (despite the arrival of imported cane sugar from the Indies). In this period, too, the scientific study of bees, their hives and their industry increased. In the 1820s Russian beekeepers started to construct sectioned hives so that individual sets of brood could be inspected. Petro Prokopovych is credited with inventing a 'queen excluder', a simple wooden board with small holes drilled in it that allows only the smaller worker bee to pass through, thus keeping the queen bee in one part of the hive (see page 64).

In the early 1850s, the Reverend Lorenzo Lorraine Langstroth, in the US city of Philadelphia, made an important discovery that would revolutionise bee-keeping. This was the 'bee space'. Langstroth observed that if bees were not happy with any space or gap in their hive they blocked it up. Any space less than 4–5 mm (about 1/8 in) wide – the room needed for a worker bee to move comfortably around the hive – was filled with propolis (bee glue). Langstroth also discovered that the wax combs were never constructed closer together than 7–8 mm (about 1/4 in). Using these measurements, Langstroth was able to create a hive in which the queen could be kept separate in her own brood box, while the other bees had the freedom of the hive. This meant that honey could be saved in one part of the hive, while the brood – the offspring (eggs and larvae) produced by the colony – was developed in another part (see also, page 63).

In 1857 Johannes Mehring invented pre-stamped foundation (beeswax sheets with a hexagonal pattern) as a template on which bees could build their combs (see page 68). Although these were slow to catch on, they were eventually combined with Langstroth's hive to complete the first modern hive and, for the first time, it was possible to harvest honey with brood mixed in with it, and to be able to remove combs from the hive without endangering the colony.

Since the 19th century, developments in apiculture have continued to allow man to make full use of the bee's labour. Meanwhile, bees have come under threat from diseases such as acarine (Isle of Wight disease), which nearly wiped out all of the British bee population in the early years of the 20th century (see page 132). Today colony collapse disorder (CCD) is the biggest threat (see page 136). While largely confined to commercial apiarists, the sudden and mysterious departure of bees from their hives is a cause of great concern. All beekeepers – big and small – must play a part to ensure, not only the survival of the honeybee, but of human life itself.

Understanding Bees

Chapter **1**

TYPES OF BEE

There are more than 20,000 species of bee worldwide, and although some of them can be kept in hives and their produce harvested, they remain wild insects that cannot be tamed. The bees we see in our gardens represent just a handful of the world's species. All bees are important to life on earth. Whether you keep honeybees in a hive or encourage solitary and bumblebees into your garden with sweetly scented flowers and plants, you can help support the environment and maintain the health and vitality of one of nature's wonder creatures that, sadly, remains under threat.

Solitary bees

Not all bees live in colonies. The vast majority are solitary bees that fly for around six to eight weeks, having spent most of their life as pupae in cocoons. The female solitary bee is fertile, and once she has mated, will lay about eight female eggs and one male one, each contained in its own cell in a small burrow or hollow that can be found in the ground, in the soft mortar between bricks or in hollow wood. To encourage solitary bees to nest in gardens – no matter how big or small – a nesting site can be made of a bundle of 15-cm (6-in) long 6-mm (1/4-in) diameter bamboo canes attached to a fence or post in a sunny spot.

The larvae emerge from their cells just as their food source is about to blossom. The first to emerge is always male. It is his task to mate with as many female bees as he can. After mating, the male bee dies and leaves the female bees to find new nesting places in order to continue the cycle of life. Unlike bumblebees and honeybees, solitary bees generally only feed on one type of plant. When that plant's season is at an end and the bee's food disappears, so does the solitary bee. Different species of solitary bee emerge from their cocoons throughout the season, feeding on different plant sources.

Bumblebees

The bumblebee, genus *Bombus*, is a frequent garden visitor and easily recognisable with its big round body and thick, furry coat. There are some 250 species of *Bombus* around the world and, thanks to its fur coat, it is one of the first bees to be seen in spring in temperate climates. However, in Britain alone, three native species of bumblebee are extinct and the remaining 22 native species live under threat from disappearing hedgerows and meadows – their favourite nesting grounds – as well as the indiscriminate use of insecticides and pesticides.

Bumblebees live in small colonies ranging from around 50 to 400 members with a queen who produces female worker bees. Bumblebees are important in pollinating early spring plants and flowers. To encourage them into gardens, a small patch of pollen-rich flowers, and even some plants that flower throughout the year, will allow the bees to feed. Only the queen bumblebee lives through the winter. Towards the end of the summer, a colony raises virgin queens and male bumblebees, both then leave the nest to find a mate. Once the males have mated they die, while the newly mated queens go in search of suitable hibernation sites. The rest of the colony dies as winter approaches.

To survive until the spring, a mated queen hibernates in undergrowth. When she emerges in spring, she searches for a suitable nesting site where she can lay her eggs and raise her colony. Such nesting sites are generally positioned below ground level in old mouse holes, burrows in the ground, or underneath paving stones. Inside the nest site, the queen bumblebee builds wax cells to house her sterile, female worker offspring. The workers gather the pollen and nectar as the colony grows.

Honeybees

Honeybees are the focus of this book. The botanical name for the honeybee is *Apis mellifera* L. *Apis* is derived from the Greek word for 'healer' while the species name, derived from Latin, *mellifera* means 'honey bearer'. The letter 'L' after the name refers to Linneaus (1707–78), the Swedish-born naturalist who originated the modern binomial system of naming plants and animals.

The *Apis mellifera* species is divided into about 30 subspecies and numerous further hybrids. Among the most important subspecies are *Apis mellifera carnica* or Carnolian bee, that origi-

nated in Central Europe. Quite docile, this honeybee is ideally suited to living in the cooler, European climates. *Apis mellifera ligustica* are commonly known as Italian honeybees, gentle bees that rarely form swarms and produce large amounts of sweet honey. *Apeis mellifera mellifera* is the name of the British black honeybee and it was this species that was devastated by acarine in 1906. *Apis mellifera capensis* is a honeybee that hales from the Cape region of South Africa and *Apis mellifera scutellata* is the Africanised honeybee. While the latter is somewhat more aggressive than its European cousins, this is often and erroneously termed 'African killer bee'.

Subspecies can and do mate with each other and produce viable hybrid honeybees that are usually unique in terms of their colour, shape and behaviour. One of the important hybrid honeybees is the Buckfast honeybee. A hybrid of the European black bee and the Italian bee this was developed in England by Brother Adam, a Benedictine monk at Buckfast Abbey in Devon, in a response to the outbreak of acarine disease that nearly wiped out the native British black honeybee.

A WORD ABOUT WASPS

Like bees, wasps buzz and sting, but while they are distant cousins, that's the only thing these two species have in common, for they are very different creatures. Wasps are omnivorous and will sting to kill their prey. Bees, on the other hand, eat only nectar and pollen. Unlike wasps, which can sting repeatedly, once bees have used their stinger, they die. Bees make their nests from wax while wasps construct their nests from chewed wood fibres. Although many people see wasps as a nuisance, there are two things to bear in mind: wasps only sting humans when threatened; and wasps never return to an old nest. Leaving an old, empty nest in place will discourage new nesting, because wasps will think another colony has got there first! Finally, wasps are also very important pollinators of plants and they dine on aphids, small flies and decaying plant matter in the garden, so they should be encouraged.

BEE BODIES

Like all insects or *hexapodia*, bees have six legs and a body, divided into a head, thorax and abdomen. They have four membrane-like wings, a pair of sensitive antennae and large, compound eyes. They don't have a bony skeleton but, instead, are held together by an exoskeleton – strong plates covered in wax and held together by a tough, yet very flexible membrane – with all their muscles attached to the insides of the plates.

Unlike humans, bees don't have blood vessels, because they don't have any blood. Instead they have a fluid called haemolymph, which is pumped around the body by a very simple heart that transfers oxygen and nutrients to the body tissues. Instead of lungs, tiny holes in the exoskeleton, called spiracles, allow air to flow into and out of a bee's body. When a bee has used up one supply of air, a large muscle in the abdomen expands and contracts to force air in and out of the body through the spiracles. Wing beating also helps to maintain the flow of oxygenated air across the spiracles, which, in turn, lead to a series of tubes (the trachea) that carry air backwards and forwards around a bee's body. The bee's thorax (or chest) is largely filled with powerful muscles, glands and with the nervous system that extends along the lower part of the body.

A bee's gut is divided into several sections and the digestive process begins with the proboscis – the long, retractable tongue that a bee uses to suck up nectar from deep inside flowers. The nectar is passed to the honey stomach via a tube that runs through the bee's thorax. In the honey stomach, the bee partially converts the nectar into sweet syrup, which is ejected at the honeycomb to make the valuable stores of honey in the hive. Beyond the honey stomach is a second stomach where nectar is digested to provide the bee with it's own sustenance and fuel, and naturally, a rectum, through which waste material is passed.

A bee's head

Bees have no brain as such but, instead, function by a series of ganglia (nerve cells), which act as processors, responding to stimuli received by sensors and, in turn, sending messages to the rest of the body. Although it's less than 1 cubic millimetre in size, this 'brain' has more nerve cells than any other animal. On either side of the head are two large compound eyes that are composed of thousands of 'simple' eyes, each one with a single lens. Scientists have discovered that some of the bee's eye cells recognise movement, while others recognise colour. In addition to the compound eyes, there are three simple eyes called ocelli. These recognise changes in lightness and darkness – for example, a sudden shadow cast over the bee. Bees don't like the darkness – which is why beekeeper's suits and veils are traditionally white or light coloured. The first ganglion processes the information received from the bee's eyes and creates a picture that the bee 'sees' – a picture that scientists believe is not too dissimilar to the one we enjoy as humans.

Other ganglia process information from the two antennae packed with highly sensitive chemical receptors that allow the bee to navigate through its environment. The antennae play a vital role in allowing a bee to recognise its queen's pheromones and to detect the scent of any alien bee or other hive predator. The sense of smell is very important to bees, and each colony has its own unique scent. It is believed that bees recognise the smell of their beekeepers, many of whom eschew perfumes and scented soaps to avoid confusing their colonies. It is even said that bees can smell the animal origins of leather shoes and watch straps — a smell that causes distress.

Bees don't bite, because their mouths are adapted for drinking and for chewing. Using their mouths they chew and place wax into position in the hive to construct the honeycombs, and for positioning the propolis that they use to seal up holes.

The bee's knees

It's not surprising that the phrase 'the bee's knees' means something pretty special, because honeybees, in fact, have some of the most evolved legs in the entire insect world. While the forelegs are pretty similar to other insects' legs, and are used to clean the antennae and the eyes, the legs also have sensory organs in the form of fine hairs, which allow a bee to make sense of where it is in the world or in the hive. The hairs also act as balancers, in the same way the inner ear in a human operates. It's on the hind legs of a bee that the clever device called the corbicula is located. This is the pollen basket or 'sac' in which pollen is collected and transported back to the hive. The pollen gets stuck on the many hairs of the bee's legs and is transferred by the front legs into the basket.

Wings and stings

Bees have four wings and, again, these are a little different from those of other insects. In flies, the second pair of wings is very small, or at least reduced in size, while in beetles, one set of wings has hardened to form a shell or case. Bees, on the other hand, have two pairs of wings and each pair is able to beat independently — which they do billions of times as they fly — by using the flexible exoskeleton to flip the wings into position. Furthermore, the front and rear wings can be hooked together to act as one big pair if needed. When a bee is at rest, the rear pair of wings fold neatly under the front pair so that it looks like the bee has just two wings. Sometimes, especially first thing in the morning or when a bee has been caught in a rain shower, the wings get too wet to fly and the bee can be seen resting in a sunny spot with its wings outspread drying off in the air.

Bee stings are made up of reinforced plates to which a venom sac is attached. As the bee delivers its sting, it leaves behind the venom sac along with part of its own body in the form of a pulsating muscle that injects the venom into the victim. Because a large part of its body cavity is now open to the air, the bee dries out internally and dies shortly afterwards.

Bee Hierarchy

Chapter 2

THE CASTE SYSTEM

Honeybees are social animals and cannot survive alone. In the summer, when pollen and nectar are abundant, a typical colony will contain a queen bee, around 50,000–70,000 female worker bees and a few hundred male drones. Each of the three castes of honeybee has a distinct function in the colony.

Worker bees

The bees we most often see buzzing around our gardens are worker bees. Inside the hive, apart from laying eggs, all aspects of a colony's wellbeing, including excreting the wax that makes the honeycombs, are looked after by these bees, which work together as a team to ensure the colony's survival. Worker bees are the smallest bees in the hive. They have shorter bodies than a queen but are often more brightly coloured and strongly marked. Worker bees also have fewer hairs than the queen, and their bodies are designed specifically for carrying pollen and honey. Although worker bees retain their ovaries and produce eggs, they are unable to mate. Furthermore, if they are allowed to grow they become drones, although only about one in a thousand drones is derived from a worker bee.

A worker bee's duties change depending on her age and physical maturity, because a newly hatched bee is not fully developed and her sting and wax glands have not matured. Worker bees begin their lives as cleaners, inspecting, cleaning and polishing the cells for their queen to lay her eggs in. They also lick the queen and, in doing, receive a chemical that inhibits the development of their sex organs. Although a number of female worker bees develop egg-laying potential, they are usually recognised by the other workers and destroyed in order to maintain the status quo in the colony. After a few days' growth, a worker bee's task is to feed older larvae with pollen and nectar. As soon as her own mandible and mandible gland have developed, she will start to feed the younger larvae with royal jelly.

The next stage in a worker bee's maturity is the development of her wax glands, located on the underside of her abdomen, near her stinger. Each worker bee has four pairs of wax glands, which secrete a liquid wax that forms white, translucent flakes. In order to produce this, the bees first fill themselves with honey and then cluster together in groups in order to maintain a high temperature as they metabolise the honey. The wax is then collected from the pockets using the rear legs and worked by the mandibles before being applied as a comb. With her wax glands, the worker bee is able to cap the larvae and honey cells and use the wax to repair or build new combs. At about two weeks old, a worker bee is ready to collect pollen and nectar from returning forager bees and place this foodstuff in the food cells.

At eighteen days old – three days before she flies out from the hive – a worker bee takes her turn to guard the hive entrance. She communicates with other bees using her senses of touch, vibration and smell. The Nasonov gland, located on the upper side of the abdomen towards the stinger, emits a pheromone, or scent, that is unique to the colony: worker bees can often be seen at the entrance to the hive with their bottoms in the air and flapping their wings rapidly. This is so she can send the scent through the air to act as a scent guide that fellow worker bees can use to navigate back to the hive. By this stage her sting has developed completely. As a gatekeeper to the hive, the worker bee is charged with keeping alien bees out and she will use her sting to bar a persistent intruder, dying herself as a result.

During the first three weeks of a worker bee's life she may also be called upon to perform the urgent task of ventilating the hive by beating her wings very rapidly: this helps to regulate the inside temperature while the fanning also evaporates the water content from the nectar, turning it into

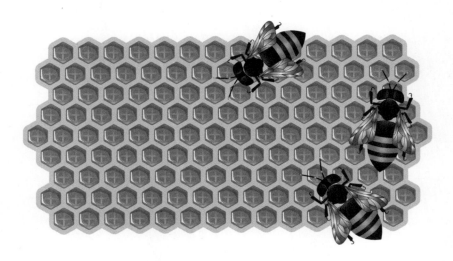

honey. At three weeks old, a worker bee is ready to begin a new phase in her short life, flying out from the hive to begin foraging for pollen, nectar, propolis and, crucially, water. Starting with a few orientation flights to allow her to fix the position of the hive from various points on her flight path, in the next three weeks she will travel as far as 3 km (2 miles) on each foraging trip, covering some 1,000 km (620 miles) in her lifetime.

Each flight is fraught with danger: she is prey to spiders and birds; her wings can be battered against the plants and flower heads on which she lands; she can fly into the path of an oncoming car and be killed. She must also face the dangers of pesticides and insecticides, all in order to carry home a cargo of nectar and pollen that weighs as much as she herself does. In theory, worker bees could live for several years, but most will die after six weeks or so from sheer exhaustion. Worker bees that are born in the late summer may be one of the 10,000 or so bees that overwinter and survive in a tight ball eating the stored honey. In spring she will be the first out of the hive and her life will end some six weeks later.

Drones

Drones start off their lives in a larger cell than worker bees and live for only around three weeks. These male bees are identifiable because they are squatter and squarer in shape than either the worker bees or the queen. Their sole function is to mate with the queen. Furthermore, they have no stinger. While the female worker bees do most of the work, the male drones, when they are not out looking for a queen on her mating flight, spend their time in the hive, eating honey and helping with the ventilation when needed. Male drones live like this for most of the summer. Unlike the workers, drones can migrate to other colonies to look for a queen. When a drone does finally mate with a queen – which happens in flight – this becomes his last act. As he dismounts, his sex organs are ripped from his body and he falls dying to the ground. By the end of the summer, any drone that has failed to mate is evicted from the hive. Once outside the comfort of the hive, unable to gather food, a drone soon starves to death.

Queen bees

Unlike worker bees or drones, a queen bee can live for several years. She spends practically all of her life in darkness, deep inside the hive and only emerges on two occasions: once to mate and, later, to swarm. Because there may be several thousand bees in a hive, you have to look carefully for the queen: she is longer than worker bees, with a more tapered body, more elongated but smaller wings, a little lighter in colour and has a pronounced abdomen that is full of eggs.

Although she has been given this regal title, a queen bee doesn't actually rule the hive, for she has no real powers. Without a queen however, the colony dies. Because the lifespan of a worker bee is only about six weeks, workers must be replaced often if the colony is to make the most of the nectar and pollen available to make honey. The queen's function is, therefore, to lay eggs in order to produce more workers. A fertile queen can lay up to 2,000 eggs a day and during her laying she is attended by a group of worker bees who feed, clean and generally housekeep for her so she doesn't have to do anything beyond laying her eggs.

In addition to egg laying, the queen also provides hive cohesion through the excretion of her pheromones. The queen's scent, known as the queen substance, keeps the worker bees happy and secure for as long as she continues to lay. Once a queen's fertility starts to fall, the chemical composition of her pheromone scent changes. This is noticed by the worker bees, who may then become aimless, listless or even agitated and aggressive. The attendant worker bees, noting the change in the queen's health begin feeding an egg with royal jelly to build up the cells into an emergency queen cell. Sixteen days later, a new queen bee emerges from the cell and, in a process called supersedure, kills her own mother and takes control of the colony (see page 105). A queenless colony will produce a number of replacement queens in cells but, usually, the first queen to emerge after sixteen days will then destroy any potential usurpers. If the colony remains queenless when winter comes, it will probably die out before the spring.

The queen is laid in a special queen cell (see page 101). Here she is fed solely on royal jelly, a glandular secretion that is packed with hormones and honey and that makes the queen grow quickly. Once the queen has emerged from the queen cell, she makes herself familiar with the domain, learning the layout of the hive and being attended by a group of worker bees that are about two to three weeks old. Just three days after she has emerged from her cell, the queen bee is ready to mate. The outside temperature for mating must be 16°C (60°F) or higher (a colony that loses its queen between November and March stands very little chance of creating a successor, because it is both too cold and it's a period when there are no drones about for her to mate with). When conditions are right, the queen leaves the hive and flies about 10 m (30 ft) into the air, followed by a number of drones. Queen bees mate with about 10 male drones (all of whom die after the act) and she returns to the hive to start her laying process in cells that have been cleaned and prepared by workers ready for her use. Bee-keepers hope that the queen will never leave the hive again, and to ensure this they often clip one of her wings to prevent her from flying out with a swarm (see page 101).

The queen backs her way into one of the cells and attaches an egg to the rear wall with bee glue. She then moves to the next cell and repeats the process, and will do this up to 2,000 times in a single day. Each egg — which looks like a small grain of rice — is laid so that it stands upright. As each egg develops over the next few days, it falls over onto its side. It takes three days for a larva to hatch from the egg, and when it does emerge it requires feeding. Worker bees feed

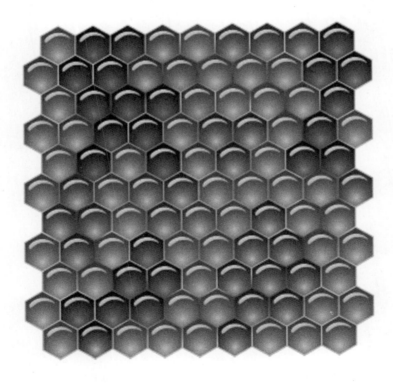

larvae with a secretion from the jaws – the royal jelly – for three days. After this time, those larvae that are not destined to become queens are switched to a diet of pollen and honey. The larva now goes through a series of instars – moults of the outer skin – and with each stage grows bigger and forms a crescent shape in order to fit into the cell. Six days later the white-coloured larva straightens itself out and stops eating. The worker bees in attendance take notice and immediately begin to cap the cell using a mixture of wax and propolis.

During the next 12 days, the larva pupates, spins a cocoon and transforms from a grub into an insect. When the process is complete – for a worker bee this takes 21 days, a drone takes 24 days and a queen bee takes only 16 days in her enlarged queen cell – the bee eats its way through the cell cap and emerges as a young bee into the hive. The area in the hive that contains the eggs, larvae and pupae is oval in shape and is called the brood nest and the more eggs the queen lays, the larger the brood nest becomes.

Making Honey

Chapter 3

THE HONEY-MAKING PROCESS

A foraging flight may take a worker bee about 45 minutes and in that time she visits up to 1,000 flower heads. This provides her with just 50 mg of nectar – roughly half her own body weight. On a good day, she makes this trip around 10 times. If each one of the 10,000 or so foraging bees in the colony does the same, some 10 million flower heads are visited and the bees gather about 5 kg (11 lb) of nectar, which, when processed by the bees, makes about 1.25 kg (2 3/4 lb) of honey.

Bee communication

The method by which a worker bee communicates sources of food to others was investigated by the Austrian zoologist, Karl von Frisch (1886–1982). In 1973 he was awarded a Nobel Prize for his work.

When a worker bee returns to the hive laden with nectar, pollen, propolis or water, she communicates to the other foraging bees the source of food, first, by climbing onto the vertical comb and allowing the others to taste it. Once they have assessed the quality and identified the substance, they watch their co-worker dance. If the source of the food is about 100 m (300 ft) away and on level terrain, the worker bee performs what is known as the 'round' dance, by flying round rapidly in a circle first to the left, then to the right: the faster the dance, the richer and closer the food source is to the hive.

A food source that is further away requires more detailed information (such as direction and exact distance) and this is given through a second dance called the 'waggle' or 'wagtail' dance. The worker bee dances straight ahead on the honeycomb while waggling the tail end of her rump backwards and forwards. She then turns and circles back – without any waggling – to the start of the straight line and dances along it again, waggling as she goes. When she reaches the top of the line, she turns the opposite way and returns to the start. It's the number of times that she 'waggles' along the straight line within a given time period that indicates the distance of the food from the hive. The slower the waggling, the further away it is: a waggle that lasts a couple of seconds seems to indicate a food source about 2,000 m (1–1 1/4 miles) distant.

The direction in which the source of food is to be found is conveyed by the direction of the dance in relation to the position of the sun. If you image the honeycomb as a clock face, if the bee's head points upwards to 12 o'clock, the message is that the food is on a line directly towards the sun. (If the food source is in the opposite direction, the bee's head would point to the 6 o'-clock position). As the sun changes position in the sky (by about 15 degrees per hour) the bee alters the direction of its dance to compensate. When the new foragers fly out of the hive, they check the position of the sun before flying off to locate the food source. Even if the sky is overcast, a small break in the clouds is enough for the bees to determine the position of the sun because they are able to detect the vibrations of polarised light in the patch of blue sky. And even when the cloud is unbroken, bees can still sense the sun's position because they are able to sense ultraviolet light.

Nectar

Honey begins as nectar, a sugary syrup that is found in the flowering parts of pollinating plants. The nectar attracts bees and other insects who then inadvertently also collect the plant's pollen, which is then transferred to other flower heads, ensuring the reproduction of the plants species. The high-energy nectar provides worker bees with fuel and food during their foraging, but they also collect it for making honey in the hive. Each species of plant produces a different nectar, and it is this that gives honey its flavour, colour and consistency.

A worker bee transports nectar in her honey stomach. While she works, she secretes enzymes that start the process of converting the complex sugar of the nectar into a simpler form. Once back at the hive, the worker bee regurgitates the nectar and passes it to a house bee, who continues the conversion process by placing a drop on her proboscis and chewing it while exposing it to the air. It may take the house bee 20 minutes to chew on a single droplet in order to reduce the water content of the nectar before hanging the droplets up inside a cell. The process is repeated continuously until

the cell is full. Meanwhile, other worker bees fan the honey by beating their wings rapidly to dry it further, reducing the water content to about 19 per cent, which thickens the honey. Once the bees are happy with the water content, they cap off the cell with a thin layer of fresh wax, preserving the honey inside for future use.

The honey is used to feed growing larvae and the foragers. It also gives the house bees enough energy to keep the brood areas of the hive warm or cool depending on the weather. The brood areas must be kept at a constant temperature of 35° C (95° F). When it is cold outside, the house bees huddle together and shiver to maintain the temperature. When the outside temperature is too high, the house bees have to beat their wings rapidly to circulate cooler air in the brood areas. Honey is also needed to stimulate the wax glands. During the course of one year a colony needs around 120 kg (265 lb) of honey in order to function. So, the worker bees must collect enough nectar to store and feed the colony, especially through the long, cold winter months and, in effect, it is this store that we as humans are 'robbing' for our own consumption.

Honeydew

Nectar is not the only substance collected by worker bees: both honeydew and pollen are also gathered. Honeydew is a sweet liquid excreted by certain plant-eating insects such as aphids, bark or scale insects, jumping plant lice and whiteflies. Bee colonies located close to woodland areas collect honeydew deposited by the insects that have sucked on the sap of pine, fir and spruce needles as well as from the leaf stems of deciduous trees. Excess sap hangs in shiny droplets on the needles or leaves of the trees and is collected by the bees for processing in the same way as nectar. Honeydew production begins in early to mid-July and while it is flowing, worker bees from a colony can collect as much as 2 kg (4 1/2 lb) in a day. In European countries, a distinction is made between honey made from evergreen trees – called 'forest' honey – and that made from deciduous trees, called 'leaf' honey.

Pollen

Plants need bees (and other pollinating insects) in order to reproduce, and bees also need pollen, which is rich in protein, fats and lipids, as food. Bees are the only insect designed to collect pollen – other insects simply transfer pollen from plant to plant – and the only insect that uses it as food for their young. To rear one worker bee takes 10 average bee loads of pollen (about 0.14 g), so an average colony needs about 27 kg (61 lb) of pollen to sustain it. Because the supply of pollen varies according to the weather, bees stockpile about 1 kg (2.2 lb) of pollen, roughly a week's supply, to avoid shortages.

The round and waggle dances performed by returning foraging bees tell the worker bee whether her foraging trip is to collect nectar or pollen. If she is collecting pollen, she feeds up on honey from the hive to give her fuel, plus a little extra to use as a sticky binder to glue the pollen grains together. Honeybees are pretty methodical in their pollen gathering, visiting one particular species of flower until they have exhausted the pollen supply. Each region generally has its own pollen cycle that starts in early spring (when crocuses and daffodils are in bloom), followed by spring flowering of dandelions, fruit blossoms and horse chestnut trees, followed by summer flowering of lime trees, clovers and summer plants. Late-autumn flowering of plants like Michaelmas daisies and ivy are important late sources of pollen for bees. Most pollen is yellow or orange but brick-red pollen is derived from horse chestnuts and light-green pollen from hawthorn. Beekeepers are able to tell which plants their bees are visiting by the colour of the pollen on their legs.

When a worker bee returns to the hive, she passes the pollen to a waiting house bee, who inspects a number of cells before dropping the pollen load into a suitable one and stamping it into place using her head and legs. The cell is usually located just above the brood so that it is a readily available larder from which the older larvae, nurse (newly born) bees and younger hive bees can feed. House bees add honey to the dry pollen mix to preserve the pollen, making what is called 'bee bread'. Pollen is also considered a highly nutritious food for human consumption and to this end some beekeepers use a pollen trap to collect it for themselves. The bees pass through a small opening in the trap placed at the entrance to the hive that is just wide enough to allow the bee's body to pass through, but strips off the grains of pollen from the bee's legs. The pollen then drops through a wire 'floor' in the trap into a container that is emptied daily before it is dried and eaten.

Propolis

Also known as bee gum or bee glue, propolis is a reddish or brown-black resinous substance that is collected by worker bees from plants, especially from the buds of horse chestnut, but also from birch, poplar, beech and sunflowers. Propolis is sticky at 35° C (95° F) – the ideal hive temperature – and is used by the bees to bind the nest together and glue up holes and gaps. Propolis is also an antiseptic and is used by the bees to line the walls of their cells to protect them from moulds and infection. Furthermore, it is used to mummify the dead bodies of animals (such as mice) that are too big to be removed from the hive. Propolis is often eaten by man, sprinkled over food, and is widely used for natural or holistic medicine. For centuries, too, propolis has been used as a treatment for wood: beekeepers use it to varnish the exteriors of their hives.

Water

Water is vital for bees. They need it not only to keep their bodies hydrated, but it is vital in the production of food and in regulating the hive temperature, and they need it all year round. You can often find bees in the very shallow, warm water at the edge of a pond or on a patch of damp soil taking moisture from it. Bees can't swim so they need something to stand on while they drink, such as a floating stick or leaf. Beekeepers know that once bees find a good source of water they return to it regularly, so they ensure a constant supply of fresh water near the hive.

A TASTE OF HONEY

Valued as the 'food of the gods' for centuries, the subtle flavour, scent, colour and thickness of honey is determined by the plant from which the worker bees collect nectar. In some countries honey is derived from single-source plants, such as clover (in Canada and New Zealand); acacia (eastern Europe); eucalyptus (Australia) and leatherwood (Tasmania); wild thyme (Greece); lavender and rosemary (Spain and France); buckwheat (the eastern states of North America, and from Russia and China), and orange blossom (from Florida and California). In Britain single-source honey is derived from heather and white clover, but most is derived from a blend of wild flowers including hawthorn, fruit blossoms and the clover-like plant sainfoin. Hives situated in urban areas also produce distinctive honey because lime trees and sycamores are found lining the streets and roads and there is often a greater biodiversity in parks, gardens and even on industrial sites such as railway embankments and cuttings, canal banks and even waste ground.

In the countryside, the increasing numbers of farms turning to oil-seed rape (in the US this is known as canola) as a cash crop brings both benefits and problems for beekeepers. The bees adore the bright yellow flower heads and, because the nectar is produced from early spring, this gives the bees a head start in honey making. The downside is that it produces a rather bland-tasting honey that crystalises quickly. Bees find it very difficult to eat this and can become undernourished, so it needs to be removed from the frames within a few days (see page 121).

KIND OF HONEY	PLANT ORIGIN	TIME OF YEAR FOR NECTAR	TASTE	CONSIS-TENCY	COLOUR
Acacia	Acacia tree	Mid-summer	Mild, hint of vanilla	Thin	Very clear, light yellow
Alfalfa	Alfalfa	Late summer	Delicate and fruity	Thick	Amber to beige
Basswood	Basswood (nectar and honeydew)	Mid-summer	Very aromatic	Thick	Greenish-yellow
Borage	Borage/ star flower	Mid-summer	Hint of camomile	Thin	Pale yellow
Buckwheat	Buckwheat	Early summer	Strong flavour with a hint of malt	Very thick	Deep purple-black
Chestnut	Chestnut	Late summer	Treacle-molasses taste; rich in pollen	Very thick	Dark brown

KIND OF HONEY	PLANT ORIGIN	TIME OF YEAR FOR NECTAR	TASTE	CONSIS-TENCY	COLOUR
Clover	Red, white or sweet yellow vetches	Mid summer	Creamy butterscotch	Medium	Varies from white to light amber
Dandelion	Dandelions	Spring	Hint of ammonia	Thick (crystallises quickly so harvested early)	Deep yellow
Eucalyptus	Eucalyptus trees	Summer	Hint of toffee and raisins	Thick	Light amber
Lavender	Lavender	Mid/late summer	Strong, flowery	Medium	Dark amber
Leatherwood	Leatherwood	Mid summer	Spicy, woody	Medium	Amber
Hawthorn	Hawthorns	Early summer	Rich, almond-nutty	Very thick	Dark brown
Heather	Heather	Mid summer	Hints of toffee	Very thick	Reddish-brown
Rosemary	Rosemary	Early summer	Strong with hint of rosemary	Medium	Light amber
Sainfoin	Sainfoin (a clover like plant)	Mid summer	Slightly fruity	Thin	Very pale, almost white

KIND OF HONEY	PLANT ORIGIN	TIME OF YEAR FOR NECTAR	TASTE	CONSISTENCY	COLOUR
Sunflower	Sunflowers	Late summer	Hint of lemon	Thick (crystallises quickly so harvested early)	Opaque, egg-yolk yellow
Wild thyme	Wild thyme	Late summer	Spicy, hints of thymol, very aromatic	Medium	Amber
Fruit blossom	Derived from all fruit-bearing trees and berry bushes				
Apple blossom	Apple	Early summer	Hint of apple	Thick	Light amber
Orange blossom	Orange	Late spring	Hint of citrus, very sweet	Medium	Light amber
Raspberry	Raspberry	Mid summer	Raspberry	Unctuous	White with a red hue
Summer blossom	Derived from all nectar-bearing summer flowers	Summer	Aromatic	Generally medium	Varies from golden yellow to brandy coloured
Forest blossom derived from germander	Willow, black-berry, horse chestnut (honeydew)	Late summer	Mildly spicy	Medium	Golden yellow to amber
Heath derived from heath plants	Plants including thistles and vetches	Mid to late summer	Aromatic with a characteristic flavour	Thick, jelly-like	Reddish-yellow to amber

HONEYBEE BY-PRODUCTS

In addition to the main crop of honey, a honeybee's hive also produces two further harvestable crops: beeswax and royal jelly. Beeswax is a by-product of the honeybees' honey consumption: it takes about 4 kg (8 1/2 lb) of honey for them to produce 450 g (1 lb) of beeswax. Secreted by the worker bees, from glands under their abdomen, beeswax is tasteless, odourless and almost colourless, but takes on colour and scent from the pollen and propolis that is brought into the hive. Beekeepers extract the wax from the cell cappings after they have extracted the honey (as well as scrapings from the frames and from inside the hives during the course of the year). A normally developing colony of honeybees makes or 'draws' its combs on 8 to 12 foundations during the time of one year that nectar is flowing (in winter, no wax is produced). In the autumn following the honey harvest, beekeepers take the wax from four or five combs, rearrange the remaining combs, and make use of the beeswax – as candles, dubbin (waterproofing for leather goods) and wood waxes. Commercial hive owners often sell the wax to be used in the manufacture of soaps, cosmetics, lip balms and skin preparations.

Royal jelly

This rich secretion from honeybees is also known as 'bee milk' and is one of the foods given to the colony's larvae. The amount they are served depends on their caste destiny: worker bees get only a little during the first few days of their life; drones receive more to grow their sex organs; while those grubs destined to be queen are fed nothing else. (The mature queen feeds on royal jelly and honey). The white, jelly-like substance is largely comprised of water (around 66 per cent) with proteins and carbohydrates in equal proportions and a small number of identified minerals. Many believe that royal jelly has rejuvenating powers for the human body, but this is not scientifically proven, and the belief is more likely to come from the mental association of the product with the notion of royalty. A small-scale beekeeper with two or three hives is unlikely to harvest royal jelly because of the difficulty involved, and besides, in the long term it's better to leave it for the bees.

Keeping Bees

Chapter 4

STARTING OUT

While there are some commercial beekeepers who farm bees for profit, a great many more keep a small number of hives for pleasure. Whatever your aims, you need to take into consideration how much time and space you have and to consider your true commitment to this fascinating pastime: bees are no different from any other animal, and if you intend to keep a colony then you are responsible for their care, their wellbeing and for regular hive maintenance.

If you have caught the bee-keeping bug, the first step is to read up on the subject, find your local bee-keeping group and, ideally, undertake a bee-keeping theory course. Many of these courses are available from January to April, though there will be some courses operating later in the year. Many bee-keeping clubs run their own courses in April and August. Joining a club and undertaking a course gives the novice keeper much knowledge, some confidence and a number of useful contacts.

Apiary organisations

The international association with worldwide membership is Apimondia whose main offices are located in Bucharest, Romania, and in Rome, Italy. According to Apimondia there are 1.5 million beekeepers worldwide tending approximately 12 million colonies of bees. Although the numbers might seem enormous, the association's national, regional and local bee-keeping societies across the world are very keen to attract more members, so novices can be assured of a very warm welcome.

In the United States, the state bee-keeping associations foster close contact between apiarists and scientists and produce a range of useful and informative publications. Many individual states also have specialists who can advise beekeepers. In European Union countries, interests of beekeepers are represented by COPA in Brussels, which heads up all groups involved in agricultural production. In the UK the British Beekeepers' Association (BBKA) oversees 60 different county and regional divisions, while Scotland, Wales and Northern Ireland also have their associations. You will find the full contact details of these associations at the end of this book, as well as a number of other useful places to visit for bee-keeping information and advice (see page 144).

Club membership brings a number of other benefits, not least the access to good-quality second-hand hives and equipment. In the UK, joining a local association also gives you membership of the BBKA, which in turn gives you third-party and product (i.e. honey) insurance. The BBKA also runs the official journal <I>Bee Craft<I> to which you can subscribe, issues a range of useful advisory leaflets and runs a number of modular courses leading to BBKA qualifications ranging from Basic, Intermediate through to Master Beekeeper.

BEE DISEASE INSURANCE

Your local bee-keeping association can advise you on a scheme known as Bee Disease Insurance (BDI), which is designed to pay out if your bees have to be destroyed due to a severe 'notifiable disease' (see page 130). Some areas are at higher risk than others, and BDI is compulsory as part of local membership of the association.

The Central Association of Bee Keepers (CABK) is an educational charity, the aims of which are to promote and further the craft of bee-keeping. The CABK publishes research from keepers and bee scientists and organises lectures given by national and international bee experts. In addition to the spring meeting in London and an annual conference in Royal Leamington Spa, members have the wonderful chance to enjoy the surroundings and history of the Wax Chandler's Hall in the City of London at an annual social event held each November.

Cost, time and commitment

The cost of keeping bees depends on how deep your pockets are. Buying everything brand new can be expensive, and one of the benefits of belonging to a local club is that you are often able to get second-hand hives, bee-keeping suits, gloves and veils at a fraction of their original cost. The most expensive piece of equipment you might need is a honey extractor (see page 126), but a

local bee club may have one for communal use, so do your home-work first. You'll also need a hive or two, as well as some spare parts (see pages 67–70).

With regard to time commitment, bee-keeping is essentially a seasonal practice and the time it takes varies month on month. In midwinter there is little beyond checking the hive for damage or for snow blocking the hive entrance (bees defecate outside of the hive and need to be able to get in and out at all times). The busiest time for the beekeeper is the early summer when hives need to be checked regularly to stop swarming and to add supers (see page 92), but even this takes only a few minutes with prac-tice. Once you are familiar with the procedure, the most time-consuming part of bee-keeping at this time of year is taking your protective bee-keeping suit on and off. The monthly tasks re-quired for the beekeeper are outlined in Chapter 8, but if you are simply planning on keeping bees for pleasure and honey for yourself then you won't be counting the hours spent engaged in this activity. The only problem you may face is if you plan on being away from your hives for any given time (on holiday perhaps). In such instances you need to ensure your bees are well looked after in your absence – another good reason for joining a bee-keeping club.

LOCATION, LOCATION, LOCATION

Before you start keeping bees you need to decide on where to place the hives, and while it's true you can keep bees just about anywhere, there are a few things to consider. For example, it is perfectly possible to keep bees on an urban roof garden, but con-sider what you might do when they swarm. A black cloud of 25,000 bees may cause alarm. After flying around haphazardly for about 20 minutes, the bees cluster together and look for a tem-porary resting place within 50 m (55 yd) or so of their original hive. If that resting place is on an inaccessible roof you've little chance of collecting the swarm to increase your apiary.

A small suburban garden may seem ideal because there are plenty of nectar-filled flowers nearby, but your backdoor – and that of your neighbour – may also be close to the hive. Let your neighbour know your intentions and note that two hives are acceptable in this type of garden. Any more and you would have to prove that you are not posing a hazard. In the UK there is no legislation to stop you keeping bees in your back garden or on your roof, but this may not be the case in other countries, so check first. Furthermore, it's vital that the bee colonies are of a gentle nature and that, as a beginner, you have an experienced beekeeper assess your bees before you put them in the garden.

Two hives are the optimum number for the small-time beekeeper. Should there be a problem with one hive, with its solitary queen and colony, a second hive acts as compensation. Keeping two hives also allows you to compare and contrast the relative differences in the hives' occupants, their activity and their condition. The ideal location is a rural one where there is more room and space to expand, but wherever you keep your bees, the principles remain the same: a dry, sheltered, quiet spot far enough away from people that you and your bees can go about your business in quiet harmony.

If you want to keep more than two hives, you should first become experienced and then consider setting up an 'out apiary' on a nearby farm or smallholding. If possible, go for an organic farm, as this will reduce the number of pesticides and insecticides your bees come into contact with. The majority of arable farmers or smallholders who work their land in this way would be more than happy to let you put hives on their land as it brings them the great benefit of bio-diversity and increased insect pollination.

One location not to place a beehive – unless it is protected by some sort of barrier – is in a paddock, as horses can accidentally kick over a hive with their hooves. Finally, it's true that bears like honey, but so do badgers, who tend to get underneath hives. If you have badgers in your area, consider erecting a barrier to keep them out. Skunks are more of a problem in the US, where they're not so much after the honey as the bees themselves and will scratch the front of the hive. The bees come out to defend their nest and fall prey to the hungry skunk. While a strong colony can sometimes see off a skunk assault, many weaker colonies are devastated so it's worth protect-ing the hives with fencing and by placing them on raised stands be-yond skunk height.

Beehives and allotments

If you are lucky enough to have an allotment you may be allowed to keep hives there, but you need permission first and all of the other allotment holders must agree. You then need to prove that you have insurance cover to the level set by your local council and that you are a competent beekeeper. To prove this you may be asked to show your certificate(s) from a training course and demonstrate some extended practical experience. In some instances, allotment societies ask for a minimum number of years experience but this does vary across the system, so you need to check first.

Heat, light, cold and damp

Bees enjoy a bit of morning sunshine, so placing the hive where it catches the early rays is a good idea. The sun warms up the hive and lets the bees know that the day has begun, increasing their foraging time and, in turn, the yield of honey. Although bees are strong fliers, don't site the hive entrance in the face of the prevailing wind, as this may cause a draught inside the hive and the bees would have to work harder to control the temperature to keep it a constant 35° C (95° F). While the bees do most of the work to maintain this temperature, the keeper can help by avoiding sit-

uating the hive in spots that get too hot or too cold. If the site gets sun all day, offer some shelter by planting some tall shade-casting plants or by putting up a fence. While the branches of a tree offer dappled shade, they must not droop so low that they bang on the hive when the wind blows. This will disturb and upset the bees and a high wind may damage the branch and cause it to fall on the hive.

Avoid sunken areas, which can be frost pockets – areas where cold air gets trapped – and the bees have to work hard to stay warm. While they are pretty hardy beasts and will tolerate cold, bees hate being damp. If your area is prone to damp, you should construct the hive on a good, sturdy stand that raises it off the ground by about 60–90 cm (2–3 ft). Raising the hive off the ground is also useful in that it lifts the whole hive to a more useful working height and can help stop small intruders, such as mice, from entering.

Bonfires

Make sure your hives are not located close to a bonfire (or any other incinerator that emits smoke). Smoke is a bee's early warning sign that there's a fire around and the nest is in danger (beekeepers use a smoker to move the colony out of the hive so they can inspect the frames and harvest honey). The smoke sends the bees a signal to evacuate, but before doing so they grab as much honey as they can – enough to keep each bee alive for three days while they find a new nest site. Once the false alarm given by the beekeeper is over, the bees return to their original hive. But the problem with a bonfire sited nearby, is that the smoke can continue for a whole day, and if forced from their nest for a prolonged period, the bees may not return.

Flight path

On exiting a hive, bees fly upwards in a series of increasingly large spirals in order to orient themselves in relation to the sun so they can fly off in the direction indicated to them by a returning worker bee's waggle dance (see page 30). The spiralling flight also gives them a mental aerial map of the hive surrounding, which they will use on their return flight. Heavy with their harvest of nectar, pollen, honeydew or propolis, the bees fly straight back to the hive. If your garden is bordered by a footpath or pavement where passing pedestrians walk, siting a hive close by need not be a problem: you can train the bees to fly above head height and down to the hive by positioning 1.8 m (6 ft) hedging or fencing around the hive. The very clever worker bees soon learn that it's a lot easier to fly high and then directly down to the hive rather than approaching it at low level, before then having to climb steeply over the fence or hedge – especially when they are carrying an extra 50 per cent of their bodyweight in booty.

Water

Bees need to drink and take water back into the hive to make honey, and they need it all year round. If your neighbours have a small pod or ornamental fountain, then your bees will make a beeline for it. This is fine if your neighbours don't mind, but if you want to keep your bees in your own garden, you need to provide them with fresh water near to the hive. Some shallow dishes filled with gravel, moss or peat and kept topped with water are ideal, as they allow the bees to drink without the danger of them drowning in deeper water.

PETS, CHILDREN AND DEALING WITH STINGS

Bee-keeping suits come in all sizes, including ones for children, so there's no reason why children can't become involved with bee-keeping at an early age. Cats may well sun themselves on an empty hive, but are smart enough to move on to a new place once your bees have been moved in. While dogs can be a bit more nosey they can at least be shut indoors while you open and inspect the hives. Cat, dog or child, bees are pretty good neighbours and tolerant too. Their one real interest in life is to make honey and ensure the survival of the colony. At some time it's inevitable that you will get stung. Most people react to a sting with a little localised swelling followed by a couple of days of itchiness. Some people may, however, have a more serious reaction resulting in anaphylactic shock, which can be fatal.

Bee breeders are increasingly intent on breeding strains of non-aggressive bees. The Americanised Italian bee, the Carnolian bee, and the Caucasian bees are the most popular and are especially suited to novice beekeepers and for hives located in areas of high human density. Since bees only sting when they feel threatened, it's up to you to avoid hectic or abrupt behaviour when working with your colony. You should also avoid wearing perfumes and scented soaps that might arouse the bees, and should put on the appropriate clothing when working around the hives.

If you are stung by a bee don't squeeze the sting, as this will only pump the venom into you. Instead, slide the stinger away with your finger or hive tool (the hole in the middle is a useful device for this). The stinger is barbed, so you want to slide it in the opposite direction to the way it is puncturing your skin rather than deeper into you. You could take an antihistamine tablet if you feel it's necessary. To neutralise the acid nature of the venom, apply a paste made of bicarbonate of soda and water. (Wasp stings are alkaline and need to be neutralised with acid, so apply a dab of vinegar).

WRITTEN RECORDS

Although the work a beekeeper does is quite limited and doesn't take up a great deal of time, there is one aspect of bee-keeping that must be carried out. Since 2006 in the UK, the Veterinary Medicines Directorate (VMD) has legally classed bees as 'food-producing animals'. To remain within the law, all beekeepers must complete Animal Medicines Records in the same way that all other farmers and livestock keepers do. Furthermore, the records should be available for inspection by VMD officers and kept for five years. Keep all receipts for any medications, as the VMD will want to see them so they can assess the effectiveness of particular treatments.

Most beekeepers keep two types of record: a day-to-day record (this is not compulsory but is recognised as good practice) and the compulsory Animal Medicines Record.

For the day-to-day records, beekeepers generally note:
- the health of the colony
- activity on the landing board
- the amount of food stored in the hive
- the number of frames with brood (this indicates the strength of the colony)
- signs of swarming
- supers added/removed and the reasons for this
- an estimate of the amount of honey produced by the hive in this season
- the year of the queen and whether she has a clipped wing or is marked
- date of varroa inspection, varroa count and result
- volume of syrup fed (going into winter)
- a note of any actions undertaken and any that need to be done at the next inspection

THE THREAT OF DISEASE

Outbreaks of serious diseases, such as American foulbrood and European foulbrood are, thankfully, rare. This is due, in part, to the cooperation and dedication of beekeepers for whom the welfare of their colony is paramount. In order to keep these diseases – and others (see pages 130–6) confined, it is essential that anyone new to bee-keeping should be familiar with the responsibilities outlined in the government-issued Bee Diseases and Pests Control Order.

Hives and Frames

Chapter 5

BEEHIVES

Once you have decided to keep bees, the first piece of equipment you need is a beehive. In fact, you'll need two hives in order to ensure that you don't lose your bees if they swarm (see page 101). In addition to the hive structure you'll need the appropriate number of supers and frames (see below) as well as bases and stands. For the new beekeeper, a good time to start a first colony is in the period after swarming, usually mid- to late summer, as this will give your colony time to build itself up over the remainder of the season. That way you'll be able to add to your kit over the winter months so you are prepared for the following season.

In the wild, bees build nests in inaccessible places – overhanging tree branches or rocky outcrops that are safe from animal predators. A beekeeper's hive is, essentially, an artificial environment in which the honey crop can be harvested without disturbing the bees, destroying the nest or the colony. There are a number of hives types available, but most follow a single-walled box model that, during the summer months when nectar is flowing, is increased in height to give the bees plenty of room to store their honey (see page 55).

BUYING A HIVE

The most important thing to remember when you buy your first hive is that the bees have to be happy living in it and must remain healthy. Secondly, the hive must be easy for you to work with. It needs to be light enough that you can lift it, but strong enough to carry the weight of the honey. A super can weigh around 12–15 kg (26–34 lb) and you need to be able to lift this without causing yourself injury. Although most hives are standardised, using the same models as other members of a bee-keeping society in your local area will make things easier, giving you access to second-hand supplies of boxes and feeders, lids, floors, frames, crown boards and queen excluders that fit your hives as well.

In the United Kingdom, the most common type of hive is the National hive, while in the United States and many parts of Europe, the Langstroth (or the Commercial) hive is most widely used. There are a number of other hive types available, including Smith, Top-bar and Dadant hives. There is also the William Broughton Carr (WBC) hive, which is best described as the traditional pagoda-style wooden hive with a gabled roof and sloping sides.

Single-walled box hive

By far the most common type of hive used, these are popular with both amateur and professional beekeepers. The designs vary from place to place: components of one type of hive are unique to that form, so if you buy extra frames or boxes, you need to make sure that they are compatible with the ones you already have. The name 'box hive' pretty much describes the hive's appearance, as it looks like a stack of wooden boxes and, while not quite as pretty as the WBC hive (see below) they are much easier to use and the frames have more surface area (so accommodating more bees).

All box hives work on the same principle of stackable floorless boxes that hold the frames. From the outside, they can all look pretty similar: the differences are in size as well as in whether the space for the worker bees to crawl through in order to get around the hive is above (top) or below (bottom) the frames. The location of the space makes no practical difference to the working of the hive but it is a

reminder that the various types of hive have parts that are not interchangeable.

As the name implies, a single-walled box hive is just that: it has no added protection against the elements. Traditionally, box hives were constructed of cedar wood, as the wood's natural oils help to preserve it for decades, even in extreme climates. It used to be the fashion to paint the hives and while some still do, this must be done with a nontoxic paint. Others prefer to leave the wood in its natural state.

Moveable frame hive

The ability to remove individual frames of honeycomb from the hive is a feature of modern hives. It was developed by the Russian apiarist, Petro Prokopovych, who also invented the modern queen excluder (a simple wooden board with holes drilled in it, see page 64). Modern hives are designed around the minimum bee space – the space the Reverend Langstroth discovered in the late 19th century as 4–5 mm (1/8 in) – and which is the room needed for a worker bee to move comfortably around the hive.

There are various advantages with the moveable frame hive. Firstly, it allows the hive space to be adjusted to suit the size of the colony by adding supers as they are needed. In winter, empty hive bodies can be used to store empty combs, while the honey-filled frames can be transported easily to an extractor outside the hive, doing away with the need for special transporter boxes. Finally, you get more honey because you can house a larger and stronger colony. The only real downside to the moveable frame hive is its weight: a super and all the frames full of honey can weigh as much as 20 kg (50 lb).

National hive

In Europe, beekeepers have a choice of hive, but the National hive is most widely used, especially in the UK. It is similar to the American Langstroth hive (see below) in that it consists of separate boxes to house both brood and honey. The opening of the National hive allows for the frames to be stacked parallel to the opening or perpendicular to it, and this alters the passage of air through the hive. Frames that are parallel to the opening are known as the 'warm way' while frames that are perpendicular are known as the 'cold way'. The frames in the National hive, 13 in total, are flush with the top surface of the box. The bottom surface is deeper than the ends of the frames, thus creating a bottom bee space.

Langstroth hive

Designed by the Reverend Langstroth, who constructed his prototype from some wooden champagne boxes, the Langstroth hive is the model used most widely in the United States. It consists of a rectangular bottom board with a rim 3–10 cm (1–4 in) high onto which two or more wooden boxes without tops or bottoms (called hive bodies) sit. The hive body on the bottom is called the brood chamber, while the bodies on top are used by the bees for honey storage and are called supers. On top of the hive bodies is a cover, an inner lid of insulating material (for cold weather) or a ventilation screen (a fine wire mesh fitted into a narrow wooden frame) that is inserted for transporting the bees. All the parts from the bottom board to the lid have exactly the same dimensions so they can be stacked up neatly. The hive entrance is a small rectangular hole on the front of the hive in the rim of the bottom board. With the Langstroth hive, the frames for the honeycombs – of which there are 10 – are hung into and taken out of the hive bodies from the top, making this a top bee space hive.

Commercial hive

The Commercial hive is used by commercial beekeepers. It has the same dimensions as the National hive, but is available as either a bottom bee space or top bee space hive and is often used with brood boxes situated above the queen excluder. Used to create a strong colony, the supers of Commercial hives are often simply brood boxes on top of the queen excluder in order to produce a large volume of honey – up to 23–27 kg (50–60 lb) of honey per box. To help reduce the overall weight, and stop keepers from straining themselves in the process of inspecting and harvesting, it's not uncommon to see a Commercial hive brood box with lighter weight National hive supers.

Dadant and Smith hives

The Dadant hive is one of the largest hives in use and is widely found in France and parts of Spain. It is similar to the American Langstroth hive. It too has 10 frames, is a top bee space hive and, in many instances, the parts between them are interchangeable. The Smith hive, on the other hand, is built to the same dimensions as the National hive. It has 13 frames but, importantly, is a top bee space hive because the frames come flush to the base of the box and the space for the bees to move around the frames is at the top.

Top-bar hive

The fact that bees are able to draw their honeycomb from a 'roof' – even a simple overhanging branch or stick – is exploited by beekeepers in very simple hives such as Top-bar hives. Cheap and easy to construct from local materials, these are widely used in parts of Africa and throughout the developing world. The Top-bar hive provides bees with nothing more than a simple bar from which the worker bees draw their honeycomb. Top-bar hives are only a little more complex in fact than a skep (see below), and this is how honey was made for centuries before modern moveable frame hives were

devised. In a Top-bar hive there is no way of separating the brood from the honey store, but by moving the bars around, it does make it possible to keep the brood nest at one end of the hive and the stores at the other. Furthermore, it's not possible to spin the honey out of the comb with an extractor. Instead, the honey is gathered by allowing it to drip slowly into a bucket (see page 123).

William Broughton Carr (WBC) hive

Named after its inventor, William Broughton Carr, in 1890, the WBC hive is popular in Britain, not least because of its attractive shape. Carr designed the hive to take account of the climate in Britain, hence its gabled roof and sloping walls. The WBC hive takes the same frames as the National hive, but can only fit 10 frames. It costs more than a National hive and the pagoda-like 'lifts' (the external covers) have to be taken off one at a time, along with the roof for each inspection. In the National hive, it's just the roof that comes off. Using a WBC is more fiddly, therefore, and takes a bit more time, and for the bees themselves, this can be a disruption. On the plus side, because the lifts act as insulation and as a casing for the inner parts, the brood and supers can be made of lighter, thinner wood, reducing the weight of the boxes. Furthermore, the WBC has a porch that holds the entrance to the hive. This keeps rain off and lets you slide the entrance blocks open and shut to change the size of the entrance hole.

Skeps

The skep is basically a large dome-shaped straw or wicker basket with a hole in it so that bees can get in and out. There is no base or floor, so the bees hang from the roof from which they draw – that is, build – their honeycomb. The main problem with many old hive types, such as skeps, is that they do not allow the beekeeper to inspect individual sets of broods, it's difficult to locate the queen, and the honeycomb is a mix of brood and honey. When the honey is harvested, the colony is, therefore, destroyed. Now illegal in most countries, skeps are often maintained as decorative features in gardens,

although they do come in useful for catching swarms and housing them temporarily in a nice, safe and warm place.

Leaf hives and bee houses

In addition to moveable frame hives, bees are also sometimes kept in leaf hives and in bee houses. A leaf hive consists of a wooden box subdivided by a metal grid into two equal spaces: the brood chamber below, and the honey chamber above. The mesh of the grid is large enough for worker bees to pass through, but too small for the queen, so only the worker bees can get at the combs in the upper chamber where the honey is stored.

Because the combs containing the brood nest are in the separate, lower chamber, the honey-filled combs in the upper chamber can be removed for extraction without any of the larvae being contained in them. An inch or so above the bottom of the leaf hive (and above the metal excluder grid) are racks of horizontal metal bars. The frames for the combs slide onto the bars so they are lined up vertically on the bars of the rack. When one frame is removed, the other frames can be moved along to the right or left. Unlike moveable frame hives, a leaf hive isn't worked from the top, but from behind because the frames are taken out and inserted from the side opposite the hive entrance. The rear wall of the brood chamber is made of a wooden frame housing a glass window on the inside of which is an empty wooden frame called the frame building that the bees can fill with combs. The type of cells the bees build here – worker, drone or

queen cells – indicates the 'mood' of the colony. The glass window in a leaf hive makes it possible for the keeper to observe the colony without disturbing the bees. (In a moveable frame hive, an empty frame hung next to the brood nest fulfils the same function). The entire rear side of the leaf hive is closed off with a wooden door.

One advantage of the leaf hive is that, if sited at the right height, work with the bees can be done sitting down – ideal for older or disabled beekeepers. The down side to having a leaf hive is that it must be housed inside a building – a bee house – and it requires special storage cabinets to house the frames that are not in use in winter.

Bee houses are especially common in northern Europe. In some instances they are little more than a converted garden shed, while in others they are quite magnificent 'apartment blocks' for bees, with each hive having a landing board painted a different colour to help the bees find their way to their own home. A shed offers a very useful space for all the bee-keeping equipment, but these structures are only really useful for housing leaf hives that are worked from the rear. (Moveable frame hives are worked from the top, and this needs to be done outside, in an open space).

HIVE ANATOMY

In order to understand how a hive works, the internal component parts of the hive need to be examined.

A hive is, essentially, a number of floorless and roofless boxes that sit one on top of the other and that are capable of holding 10 or more frames. The boxes come in two depths: deep boxes are called brood boxes, where the developing larvae are housed, and the shallow boxes are called supers (Latin for 'on top'), where the bees store their honey. The supers are shallow simply because it makes them a little lighter to lift when they are full of honey. The tower that the hive creates when assembled makes a footprint of about 60 sq cm (2 sq ft) and, depending on the season, will range in height from 60 cm (2 ft) up to 1.8 m (6 ft). As the summer season progresses, additional floorless super boxes are added in which the bees save the incoming nectar.

Wooden hives

Some modern hives are made of PVC or polystyrene. Both offer excellent environments for bees to live in and have better insulation properties than single-walled wooden hives. Nevertheless, most beekeepers still prefer wooden hives, especially cedar wood. These need to have their interior surfaces scorched with a blowtorch before use, which ensures that any pests or diseases lurking in the grain of the wood are killed off before the bees are introduced. Take special care around the corner and joints, as this is where mites might be lurking, and inspect the hive closely to make sure there are no cracks or warps in the wood.

There is some debate among beekeepers as to the merits of painting hives. They were often painted in the past, as some believed the colours helped the bees to locate their hives after a return flight from foraging. Others maintained that the colours were simply to identify who owned which hive. This would have been necessary if the hives were kept on common ground or placed in a farmer's orchard.

Some beekeepers maintain that wood in its natural state creates a better environment for the bees, as it is closer to the natural wild nesting environment of a tree hollow. Any condensation inside the hive evaporates more quickly because the wood isn't sealed with paint. At the very least, a beekeeper will treat the inside and outside of a hive with a non-toxic wood preserver. If you wish to paint the exterior of your hive, use exterior-quality house paint and make sure that this is completely dry and all the hive parts have been well ventilated before you introduce the colony.

The brood box

The brood box is the deep box (around 23 cm/9 in), in which the mass of bees lives and congregates around their queen. It needs to be this deep because the size of the colony will increase during the season and, at night, all of the bees need to be accommodated. Bees are one of the few non-mammalian animals that sleep. A full colony forms itself into a ball of bees in the centre of the brood box where the hive is warmest, with extras spilling over into the super. The brood box is also where the queen lays her eggs, where the brood is nurtured and fed, where the house bees clean the used cells and where pollen and honey stored for food are kept. The queen will only lay her eggs where she thinks the temperature is just right and this often produces a large semicircle in the lower half of the brood frames. Depending on your type of hive there are either 10, 11, 12 or 13 frames in the brood box and the brood nest is usually centred on the middle frames before it spreads out to fill the entire brood chamber. (Frames are discussed in greater detail on page 67.)

The supers

These are the boxes that hold the shallow super frames. Each super holds between 10 and 14 frames (depending on the hive style) and is around 15 cm (6 in) deep. This is where the bees store the honey that the keeper eventually harvests. In the course of the summer, as the colony matures and as more honey is produced, beekeepers add more supers to the hive to provide sufficient honey storage space.

The queen excluder

The queen excluder has a very long history. Originally, when man first started keeping bees, the queen excluder was made of wood with worker-bee-sized holes drilled in it. Today the queen excluder is a wire mesh, and serves to allow worker bees to pass between the brood box and the super box above, while preventing the larger-bodied queen bee from moving between the two and laying her eggs in the super because the beekeeper wants the super solely for honey storage.

The beekeeper decides where to locate the queen excluder. In a new hive, it is the usual practice to allow the bees to fill all the brood frames with brood and honey

first, and then to position the queen excluder so that it separates the brood from a single super, where the workers are then able to draw the honeycomb on the wax foundation sheet (see below). With the queen excluded from the smaller frames, these contain only honey and, once this box is filled, the queen excluder is placed on the top of the first super. This results in a hive with a brood box and a super with a honey-comb reserved for the colony's winter supply, and a queen excluder that separates the hive from the second super, which contains honey for the beekeeper's use. In most situations, a colony will only require the first honey-filled super to maintain them over winter.

Crown board

Above the supers is the crown board, which is used for keeping the colony intact. The crown board seals the topmost super box and its main purpose is to help keep heat inside the hive, which needs to be a constant 35° C (95° F) regardless of outside temperature. The crown board is usually made of wood but there are Perspex and glass versions, and while these must be replaced in winter to act as insulation, in the summer, see-through crown boxes do allow you a small glimpse of life in the hive without disrupting the inside temperature too much.

Some crown boards are solid and make an excellent place for keeping hive records. Others have a hole at the centre, which enables you to feed the bees by means of a feeder without removing it (see page 77). The hole can also be used for the insertion of a Porter bee escape. At the end of the summer, when the honey is harvested from the supers, they first need to be cleared of bees. The Porter bee escape acts as a one-way valve, allowing the bees to exit through the crown board hole but without allowing them back into the hive.

Lid or roof

The lid or roof of a hive protects the whole structure from the weather. It can be a gable roof, as on a WBC hive, or flat, as on a National hive (see pages 56 and 59). Flat roofs are normally made of thin metal and some have holes in them to provide ventilation. The roof overhangs the topmost super and the two form a locked unit. Many beekeepers paint the roof of a hive and some also place a large stone on top to anchor it.

Strap

It's often a good idea to secure a hive to its stand using a webbing strap – ideally one with a metal locking device, because a knot is difficult to manipulate with bee-keeping gloves on. A locking device goes a long way, too, in deterring human thieves and vandals from stealing or damaging your hives. A strap is vital for stopping the wind from blowing the top off the hive and to stop it toppling over, especially if your hive is constructed of lightweight material. Pass the strap over the top of the hive and all the way around all of the boxes and under the hive stand (which itself should be secured to the ground).

Floor

Hives used to have a solid wooden floor of the same dimensions as the hive and, while some beekeepers continue to use them, recent research into hive ecology has found that varroa mites that fall to the solid floor can climb back into the hive and reinfect bees (see page 30). The floors of many modern hives are now constructed from open-wire mesh through which the mites fall to the ground outside the hive. The mesh floor has the added advantage of providing increased ventilation while also providing sufficient protection for the underside of the hive. For hives with solid floors, a varroa screen – a piece of mesh sitting between the brood box and the hive floor – can be fitted to deal with the mites. The floor of the hive also accommodates the hive entrance. This is fitted with a block – a moveable piece of wood – used to increase or decrease the size of the entrance.

Stand

A solid, sturdy stand not only raises the hive off the ground to prevent damp, it also helps to keep mice out of the hive and prevents the entrance from becoming blocked by long grass. The main purpose of the stand however is not really for the bee's welfare, but for the keeper's benefit, as it raises the hive to a more manageable height for working. A hive stand need not be a fancy affair: an old, small table or even a wooden crate is fine as long as it is strong enough to take the weight of the hive with the brood box and four supers loaded with honey. Ideally, the stand needs to raise the base of the hive about 60–90 cm (2–3 ft) off the ground so that the top brood box is at a suitable height to make lifting them as convenient as possible. It's a good idea to make sure your stand is firmly anchored to the ground so it can't be lifted or knocked over by high winds or animals.

Landing or alighting board

Flying bees find it much easier to gain entrance to their hive if it is fitted with a landing or alighting board (the terms are pretty much interchangeable) fitted to the base of the hive. Without one, the bees have to align themselves with the entrance while in flight. This can be difficult in strong winds or when the entrance has been narrowed off to prevent a cold draught or to keep mice out. Some beekeepers with a number of hives in close proximity to each other, paint each of the landing boards a different colour to help the bees identify which hive is theirs.

FRAMES AND FOUNDATIONS

Moveable frames have been in use in hives since the 16th century and make it possible for beekeepers to remove individual combs for inspection without disturbing the bees unduly. They come in two sizes, one that fits the deeper brood box, and one that fits the shallower supers. The frames in the supers are the ones that hold the honeycomb for harvesting. Modern frames are designed for quick and easy removal. The frames you will use will depend on the hive you have (see pages 56–9). British national frames also fit WBC and Smith hives, while Langstroth, Dadant and Commercial hives have their own specific frames.

Frame spacing

There are three basic systems for keeping frames evenly spaced throughout the brood chamber and supers. The space or gap that bees need to crawl through freely – the bee space – is about 6 mm. Conventional, or standard, frames use spacers that slot on to their ends to keep the frames the correct width apart. These spacers come in two sizes: smaller ones for the brood box, and large ones in the supers. Spacing the frames further apart in the supers allows the bees to draw out the wax to make a single frame wider and hold more honey (it takes less time to harvest honey from a few wide frames than it does from several thinner frames).

Spacers are made of metal or plastic and come in a range of colours. The colour coding was originally devised to allow a beekeeper to identify the year in which a frame was created. Nowadays, it is more often used to help the beekeeper remember the sequence in which the frames should be returned to the brood chamber. Although honeycombs are beautifully hexagonal in plan, bees do tend to sculpt when they draw out combs, so some might be a little higher than others. This means that the space between the frames is not always uniform but likely to have a curved shape to it. Getting the frames back in the right order sequence ensures that these spaces are maintained.

An alternative to using coloured spacers is to use frames built in such a way that they fit into predetermined slots. This system only works in supers because, when you work in the brood box, you need to be able to slide the frames about as you work.

A variety of frame types allow the more experienced beekeeper greater control over honey production. In the first year or so of bee-keeping, however, the newcomer is best served by self-spacing or Hoffmann frames. With a Hoffmann frame, it is impossible to make the mistake of placing too many or too few frames in each hive, because the frames are spaced perfectly apart by an extra thickness of wood at the top of the side bars. This spacing – often called Hoffman spacing – is usually 3.8 cm or 3.5 cm (1 1/2 or 1 3/8 in) centre to centre.

Foundation

Frames hold a template from which worker bees draw (build) their combs. This template is called 'foundation' and is made of beeswax. Bees will not draw a comb from any other surface. Foundation was invented by Johannes Mehring in 1857 and is now bought stamped with worker-bee-sized cells (although you can also get foundation stamped with larger, drone sized cells. Foundation has a reinforcing wire running through it (although you can also buy unwired foundation) and there are two types. In one foundation the wire forms a letter 'M', while in the other, the wires are laid singly with their ends appearing at the top of the wax sheet. The latter are more common in the US. In the M-style foundation, commonly used in the UK, the foundation sheet is inserted into the frame so that the letter 'M' is upright.

ASSEMBLING FRAMES

Although quite simple in design, modern frames have to be assembled from several parts before they can be used in a hive. Whatever the size or style of your hive, the basic principles remain the same: pre-wired, pressed beeswax foundation is sand-wiched between pieces of wood that maintain the bee space inside the hive and allow the keeper to remove the frame for inspection. The same principles apply to both brood box frames and super frames.

You can, of course, build your own frames from scratch. If you do, you will need to make sure the wood is the standard thickness for frames and that the frames are constructed exactly to the dimensions of the hive. Such wood is generally available from suppliers of bee equipment along with the water-insoluble glue and pins needed to fix the corner joints.

Frame elements

A frame is made up of a top bar, two sidebars, two bottom bars, and nails that hold them all together. The top bar also has a holding or trapping bar and you need to re-move this before assembling the frame. (You reattach it later to hold in the founda-tion securely.

1) Using a penknife or similar, gently prise out the loosely attached strip of wood (the holding or trapping bar) from the top bar. You will eventually nail this back into place. Take care not to split the wood.

2) Attach the two sidebars to the top bar with the grooves facing inwards. This should be a tight fit.

3) On the side of the frame that has the thicker side of the top bar, place one of the bottom bars into the sidebars. Square up the frame and nail the pieces together.

4) Check the frame is still square after nailing and adjust as necessary. The frame is now ready to receive the foundation.

5) If you are using an M-wired foundation (see above), gently bend the three top loops to 90 degrees and the two lower loops back up on themselves so they won't protrude from the bottom of the finished frame. On other wired sheets, do the same to the ends of the single wires. Bend them over the back of the surface of the foundation sheet, making small loops along one edge – this will be your top edge.

6) Turn the frame upside down so it rests on the top bar with the sidebars sticking upright.

7) Insert the foundation into the grooves of the sidebars. If you are using M-wired foundation, use the edge that has three loops of wire as the top edge. Work slowly and carefully so you don't warp or bend the foundation.

8) Once the three top hoops are touching the top bar, fit the second bottom bar to hold the foundation in place.

9) Replace the holding/trapping bar on the top bar and secure it by hammering three pins diagonally through the holding/trapping bar and the three wire loops. (On straight-wired foundation use as many pins/nails as you have loops along your top edge.)

10) Finish by carefully driving a pin into each joint to make sure the whole frame is secure, checking at each stage that it remains square.

For unwired foundation, insert the foundation into the frames and hold it in place by pinning/nailing it to the first bottom bar. The bottom of the foundation should sit on the bottom bar but not protrude out of it. Fit the second bottom bar, and then the holding/trapping bar. Pin the joints all round to secure.

Now all you have to do is make up the correct number of frames to fit your hive's brood box and its first super. You'll be making further super frames later, because once the season starts in earnest, you'll need to add more supers and with more frames to store more honey!

Bee-keeping

Chapter 6 Equipment

THE RIGHT TOOLS

In addition to your hives, you'll need a few other pieces of bee-keeping kit. Having the right equipment and clothes for the job will ensure that you feel safe and confident around your bees. The calmer you are, then the calmer your bees will feel as you work on their hive, and calm bees are less likely to sting.

Bee-keeping suit

Protective bee-keeping suits are designed not only to reduce stings to the keeper but, importantly, to present the keeper to the bees in as non-threatening a way as possible. An all-over bee-keeping suit is a wise investment. Usually made from white cotton, it is zipped down the front and has a veil hood attached. Its smooth surface is designed to stop bees getting caught in folds and creases of fabric, while the veil stops bees flying in your face or becoming tangled in your hair. Such suits offer an extra layer of fabric to help guard against any stings that do occur (and they will!). There are alternative (but more expensive) lighter-weight suits made from polyester. These have a veiled hood that can be unzipped at the front neck so you can lift it over your head and let it lie on the back of your neck.

Suits come in different sizes – including those for children – and some manufacturers offer a tailoring service to custom-fit a suit to your body size. Bee-keeping suits can be expensive, so do shop around, or perhaps ask local club members if they have spare or old suits they'd like to sell on. A cheaper option is to buy a hat with a veil attached that covers the neck and shoulders and can be tucked into a shirt or jumper. These offer good protection around your head and don't interfere with your field of vision. You can buy separate over-trousers and smocks if you find these more comfortable.

If not wearing an all-in-one white bee-keeping suit, it is best to avoid dark-coloured or textured clothes. The hairy texture of some fibres means that bees catch their hairy legs on the wool, which makes it difficult for them to fly off. Bees also naturally climb upwards into dark spaces. If you leave your cuffs, collar and ankles 'open', bees will climb up and explore, and a bee that gets trapped, stressed or near your strange-smelling skin will sting. Socks are a must, as the skin on the ankles is very thin and a bee sting there feels 10 times worse than anywhere else. The alternative is to wear rubber boots and tuck your trousers into them.

A bee-keeping suit should be laundered regularly using a scent-free soap or detergent. Smelling of the artificial scents of meadows and such confuses a bee's highly developed sense of smell. Most beekeepers don't wear perfumes or aftershaves when tending hives, as bees can mistake this for a nectar source. Regular laundering also importantly keeps a bee-keeping suit clean and prevents infections being passed from hive to hive.

Beekeeper's gloves

Another part of the body requiring protection is the hands. Traditional beekeeper's gauntlets are made of super-soft goatskin and offer complete protection. However, they are also a little difficult to keep clean, which is vital for the health and hygiene of the hives. Even the best-quality leather gauntlets make it a bit difficult to feel around the hive and to manipulate components. Household rubber gloves work just as well, but many beekeepers use disposable latex gloves, which offer greater touch and can be changed regularly to maintain good hygiene around the hives. Very experienced beekeepers eschew gloves completely – their experience allowing them to move slowly, gently and very calmly among the bees without getting stung.

Smoker

After a bee-keeping suit, the most expensive piece of kit is probably the smoker. It is worth buying the best-quality smoker you can afford, as it will need to work quite hard. There are several styles available, but they all operate on the same principle: the chamber is filled with burning material – wood shavings, dried grass clippings, pine needles or paper – and once it is well lit, the lid is closed. Cool – not hot – smoke is then pumped gently through the funnel using bellows. You need to pump gently to prevent flames popping out of the end of the funnel. A whiff of smoke is all that is needed for the bees to think there is danger. They gorge themselves on three days' supply of honey and quit the hive. They will be sleepy after their honey feast and are not as aggressive as when they were hungry. This is why the smoker is used – a blast of cool non-acrid smoke gives the bees enough of a scare to make themselves busy, so allowing you to get on with the work of inspecting the hive. Once the bees realise that it was a false alarm, they return to the hive and to normal activity.

Hive tool and disinfectant

The hive tool is a masterpiece of design – a shaped piece of metal that is flat and sharp at one end and hooked at the other. The sharp end is used for scraping away comb and queen cells from the sides and bottoms of frames, while the hooked end is used as a lever. You'll need this tool, because bees tend to stick together most of the hive parts with propolis, gluing the frames, sticking the supers to the boxes below and the crown board to the super. Use the hive tool gently to prise and lift away one part from another. This is also a handy tool for separating the holding bar from the top of a frame (see page 69). Most hive tools also have a hole pierced through them (a teardrop shape is best), which you can use to suspend the hive tool on a nail in storage. It's also handy for removing stings (see page 50). To maintain hygiene and to avoid spreading infection from one hive to another, you must wash the hive tool after each use and between different hives. Use a solution of proprietary non-aromatic disinfectant.

Beekeeper's brush

A beekeeper's brush is a long-bodied, long-handled, soft-bristled brush, used for removing bees from your bee-keeping suit when you have finished your hive work. The brush is also used for handling swarms, gently coaxing them into a skep or box (see page 75).

Thermometer

A thermometer, strategically placed near the hive, allows you to check the outside air temperature quickly. Inside, the bees maintain the hive at a very cosy 35°C (95°F). If the outside air temperature is lower, this rushes in and cools the hive, after which the bees have to work hard to bring it back up to the correct warmth. The thermometer is useful because, at particular times of the year (late autumn and spring when you make your first inspection of the season) the temperature outside should be 15°C (59°F) or above to avoid chilling the bees too much.

Petroleum jelly

Bees seal up any space that is less than 6 mm with sticky propolis (see page 35), which means it can become a little difficult to separate surfaces within a hive. Covering abutting surfaces with a smear of petroleum jelly or a solution of liquid paraffin and beeswax stops bees gluing up these surfaces and makes them easier to separate and work with.

Rubber or cloth squares

Although not essential, these are very useful items. They are simply squares of cloth or rubber cut to the same size as the open top of the hive. While working on a frame, or if you have to move away from the hive for a short period, you can cover the open and exposed hive with a cloth or square. This makes the hive dark again, protecting the bees from bright sunshine or even a shower of rain.

Skeps

Bees are amazing navigators and are able to distinguish which hive is their home, even if two or more hives are located close together. Sometimes it is necessary temporarily to move a hive away from its original location. At such times, the bees are likely to fly back to where their entrance was originally. To keep those bees safe and happy until you return their home to its rightful spot, you need a skep. (A cardboard box with plenty of ventilation slits all round and a lid will work just as well). A skep gives the bees a nice, quiet, dark place to shelter. When you return the hive to its original spot, you can shake out the skep or use a beekeeper's brush to encourage the bees back into their hive.

Feeders

Two or three times during the course of the year, bees need feeding. This generally occurs in the late autumn, once you've harvested much of their stored honey, and in the spring. A first flowering in spring brings welcome nectar, but in temperate climates, all too often this brief bright spell of warm weather is followed by chill winds and rain that prevents the bees from foraging. They are forced to rely on their dwindling supplies to feed themselves and their increasing brood. This is the time of year when bees are most likely to starve.

Bee feed is a strong solution of sugar and water (in autumn) and a slightly weaker solution in spring (unless the weather is set to stay poor for some time when it starts strong before easing off to a weaker solution). The weaker spring solution tells the bees that nectar is back in flow and encourages the queen to step up her laying.

There are a number of types of feeders available, including circular, contact, frame and tray feeders. The most common type is the circular feeder. Cheap and easy to clean, this holds about 1 litre (about 2 pints) of sugar solution. Inside is an inverted plastic cup, which restricts the bees' access to the main reservoir so they don't drown. Be careful not to lose this and never use the feeder without it. The feeder can be placed on top of the crown board if it has holes in it (in which case you can fill the reservoir without opening the hive, but it can be placed on top of the frames themselves so the bees can get at the feed more easily. For more information on feeding bees, see pages 107–08.

Notebook and pen

You'll need these to record what you did in the hive and when you did it. Don't be tempted to rely on memory, even with just one hive. You need to make a note of the dates you made varroa treatments and it's worthwhile making a note, too, of the manufacturers' treatment batch numbers. Remember that, in the UK, and in many other countries, bees are legally classed as food-producing animals and, as such, scrupulous

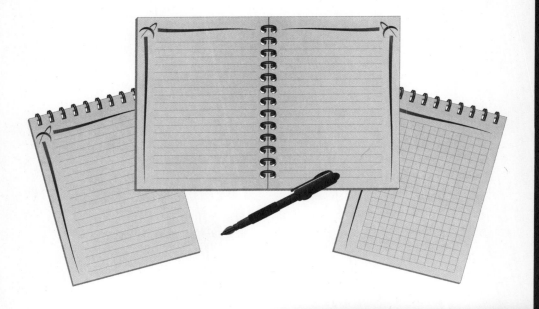

records of any medicines and treatments must be maintained. Modern technology allows the contemporary beekeeper to use a host of digital aids for keeping records: voice recorders, digital cameras, and so on. See Written Records on page 51 for details of what things you should be recording in your notebook. Records do not have to be complex, just a list of important things that you can put a tick or 'OK' next to, along with the date.

FOR THE HONEY HARVEST

The process for extracting honey is dealt with in greater detail in the section Harvesting Honey (see pages 119–28), but in terms of equipment you'll need an uncapping knife (for slicing the cappings off the cells in which the honey is stored), plenty of clean jars and lids, sieves, some clean buckets (for honey and for beeswax scrapings) and an extractor. The extractor can be manual or electrically operated, which can be expensive, but you may be able to borrow one from a club. You'll need to think about where you are going to do your honey harvesting: bees (and wasps) can smell honey from a long way off and will be attracted to it. Consequently, your harvesting needs to take place in a bee-free zone. You can do it in the kitchen, but be warned, it'll take up space, it'll take time and it'll be very, very sticky.

These are pretty much the essentials. You may like to contain and carry your smoker, hive tool, clean gloves, notebooks, pens and other paraphernalia in a shallow basket or trug. This will keep everything tidy and to hand. There are other items that are used for specific tasks in the hive – such as a queen cage and bee paint – and you will find more information on these in the section on maintaining your beehive (pages 95–118).

Chapter 7 Bringing Your Bees Home

CHOOSING YOUR BEES

Once you have selected the location for your hive, set it up, furnished yourself with all the equipment you need and, importantly, armed yourself with plenty of knowledge about bees and bee-keeping, you need to choose your bees. There are many ways of acquiring your first colony: from commercial suppliers via advertisements in bee-keeping magazines, from recommendations from other beekeepers and club members or even from a swarm provided by a bee-keeping association. Furthermore, your first bees can come in a variety of forms – a nucleus (nuc), a package or a full colony (see below).

Preparing the hive

Prior to acquiring your bees, it's important to set up the hive correctly, because once the bees have moved in, it's very difficult to move the hive. Position the hive so that the entrance faces away from strong prevailing winds, as this will cut down on draughts and stop rain from being blown into the hive. Make sure that there is plenty of space for you to work at either side of the hive to avoid blocking the entrance for foraging bees on their return.

You need air to circulate freely inside the hive. If your hive is in a sheltered location, position the frames at an angle of 90° to the hive entrance – that is, running from front to back. This is referred to as the 'cold way'. If your hive is located in a more exposed site you should position the frames, running parallel to the entrance – that is, from side to side, or the 'warm way'.

When to buy bees

The best time to buy bees (or take over a colony) is in the spring, as this means that you will be able to harvest some honey in your first year. The benefit of belonging to a club or association is that it is easy to discover who is selling a new or established colony. Because of the bees' natural work and life cycle, the window of opportunity is quite short and demand often outstrips supply. It's worthwhile contacting your bee supplier well in advance in the preceding autumn or winter to make your requirements clear and place an order.

WHAT TYPE OF BEES?

In Europe, North America and Australasia, the two most common bee types are *Apis mellifera ligustica*, known as the Italian bee, and *Apis mellifera carnica* known as the Carniolan bee, easily identified by the grey bands on its abdomen. Both types are ideally suited to the new beekeeper, but the Carniolan bee does have certain advantages.

Carniolan bees are exceptionally gentle creatures – in a short time you will be able to work around the hive without gloves – and they remain in the combs without becoming excited or agitated when you are working in the hive. This is an especially useful character trait when you are searching out the queen bee, as more excitable bees often retreat to the hive walls or dark corners when you remove a comb. Carniolan bees also develop their brood quickly, which means that a colony soon increases in size (and with it, honey production). Finally, because of selective breeding, the Carniolan bee adapts very well to different conditions, such as different hive sizes and new locations.

There are three ways in which you can get your bees: as a nucleus (nuc); as a package, or as a full colony. If you obtain your bees from a swarm, you don't really have the option of specifying the breed, but if you are buying your bees as a nuc or package you can search out suppliers of your preferred breed.

A nucleus (nuc)

A nuc consists of around 10,000 worker bees, a laying queen and a brood on five frames, and is often recommended as the best option for the novice beekeeper. It comes in a nuc box, a small, temporary hive used for transportation. The box usually has a fixed floor, a small entrance hole that is normally plugged up with a bit of foam, cork or rolled up newspaper while the bees are in transit. The roof is detachable and can be removed and replaced with a wire mesh to increase ventilation during transit, to stop the bees becoming overheated. As well as the workers and queen, the nuc comes with a foundation, some brood, pollen and honey. They all remain in the small hive for around a week until they start running out of space. During this time the queen is busy laying eggs and the colony is expanding quickly. All you do with a nuc is transfer the five frames into your hive. This means the queen bee's natural cycle of laying and the worker bees' routines of housekeeping and nursing are not disrupted (see pages 22–30).

A package

A package has the same number of worker bees as a nuc, and a queen, but does not come with a brood or any frames. Buying a package of bees is, therefore, less expensive than buying a nuc. The queen and 10,000 worker bees come housed in a screened box with a tin of feed. Because the queen and the workers come from different colonies, the queen has her own royal apartment in a separate screened cage. Her smell can permeate to the workers so they get used to her without harming her and they can feed her through the screen. It takes a few days for the workers to get used to their new sovereign and accept her as their own, but once they have done so, they all live together in harmony. A package of bees can be delivered to you by courier, but do make sure that you are there to receive them. If possible aim to pick them up yourself from a local source, which is less stressful for the bees.

The main disadvantage of a package is that it doesn't come with a developing brood, so it takes around three weeks before the colony starts producing young bees. Note that a worker bee's lifespan is only three weeks itself, once it starts to forage outside for pollen and nectar (see page 32), so your small colony of packaged bees will reduce in size before old foragers are replaced with new ones. This means you effectively lose three weeks in the honey production cycle.

Full colony

A full colony, the most expensive option, has around 50,000 worker bees ready supplied in a working hive. While this may appear to have advantages – especially if you are very keen to get started – there are several considerations to take on board. Firstly, it takes a time to become confident around bees, and starting with a smaller number of bees (as in a nuc) allows you to see what's going on in the hive more easily and become familiar with working around bees. You also really need to make sure that the hive is free from infestation and disease. Taking charge of a complete, fully working hive is something that is best delayed until your third year of practical bee-keeping. By this time you will have a much better knowledge of spring and autumn feeding, spring-cleaning the hive, and will have dealt with swarming bees.

MARKING THE QUEEN

When you buy a nuc, or package, it's well worth paying a little extra for a queen bee that's already marked, so that you can instantly tell whether she is still of a good age for laying viable eggs (see also, page 25). Marking the queen helps to spot her in a busy hive: you want to know that she is still there and has not left the colony (either in a swarm or by dying) and that she is fit and well and not damaged in any way. Since you, as the keeper don't want to injure her in any way during your hive inspections, being able to spot her easily means you can isolate the frame she is on while you examine the others. If the queen isn't already marked, you can do it yourself, although this is easier said than done, because she is usually surrounded by hundreds of her attendants and doesn't like the light.

You'll need some specialist paint from your bee supplier and some way of holding the queen safely and gently while marking. There is a device called a clip queen catcher that you can use, but more experienced apiarists simply hold her between their fingers. The simplest way is to contain the queen in a queen cage and mark her through the bars using a fine, soft brush or a matchstick dipped in the paint of the appropriate colour (see below). The idea is to trap the queen on a frame and hold her still for a short time while you dab a spot of paint on her thorax. Once the paint is dry, release the queen back into the colony.

The colours that are used for marking the queen bee follow an internationally recognised system based on the number that ends the year in which the queen was born.

Years ending in:	0 & 5	1 & 6	2 & 7	3 & 8	4 & 9
Colour marking:	Blue	White	Yellow	Red	Green

So, a queen born in 2009 will be marked with green and one born in 2010 will be marked with blue. Since a queen bee lives only for five years, the colour she wears betrays her age immediately.

SETTLING BEES INTO THEIR HOME

However you acquire your bees they will be tired and hungry after their journey and so need a good meal to give them energy to move into and set up their new home. Watching – and listening to – the bees at this stage tells you lots about their mood and wellbeing. Don't be alarmed if they sound angry; they'll soon calm down when they have cooled down a little and had some fresh air. Once the foragers have sought out supplies of nectar and come home with back legs laden with pollen, you know that they are happy and busy bringing food into the hive.

If you purchased a nuc in a five-framed nuc box, the first step is to place the nuc box on the site where the hive will be located and leave it there for 24 hours. Where you have an empty hive awaiting the arrival, move it out of the way and place the nuc box on the floor of that hive. Give the bees a chance to settle down and, importantly, to get their bearings. Unblock the entrance to the nuc box but position a clump of grass or a bit of leafy branch so it partially blocks the entrance. This forces the bees to take a little more time to leave the nuc, enabling them to get familiar with their new location.

First feed

In this first 24 hours, you can busy yourself preparing a first meal of sugar solution for your bees when they move into their new hive.

Sugar solution is similar to nectar and is a good supplement to a bee's diet when food is scarce or they need a bit of extra energy. The solution is very easy to make: it's simply white cane sugar dissolved in warm water. The strength of the solution varies according to the reason or season: in autumn bees need bulking up for the long winter, so the solution is quite strong. In spring and when you are hiving a nuc, the solution needs to be weaker as an indication to the bees that there is nectar flowing outside. They will know that they should be out and about gathering it and not preparing for the winter.

A strong solution is made using a ratio of 2 parts sugar to 1 part water – for example, 2 cups of sugar to 1 cup of water. Warm water speeds up the dissolve, but make sure the solution is thoroughly cool before feeding. A weaker solution is a ratio of 1:1. In terms of quantity, for your new nuc of 10,000 workers, you'll need about 2.25 litres (4 pints) of weak sugar solution to set them right and on their way. Once you have made your solution, fill your smoker and give it a practice run ready for the next day.

Transferring bees from a nuc into a hive

The best time to begin transferring bees from a nuc into a hive is in the evening, the day after their arrival. The process involves moving the five frames containing the nuc box into the middle of the brood box of your hive. Put on your bee-keeping suit and gloves and light your smoker – do this before raising the hood on your suit or putting your gloves on, because these make it harder to strike and extinguish a lighted match or lighter.

Walk slowly over to the nuc. The majority of foraging worker bees will have returned home by now. Direct a small puff of smoke at the entrance to the nuc box and move it gently

away from the hive site. The smoke will have set the bees off on their gorging inside and they will be unaware that they have been moved. This gives you time to put the hive in position.

Remove the lid and have an empty brood box in position on the hive floor. Bring the nuc box back close up to the hive and, using your hive tool, carefully prise off the roof of the nuc box. Next, use the hive tool to lever out one of the frames from the nuc box: remember the bees will have glued it down with propolis. Start levering with a little bit of pressure and gently increase it when you feel the frame starting to come away. Be careful not to make sharp, jerking movements, as the vibrations will alarm the bees.

Lift the first frame from the nuc box – bees and all – and place it in the centre of the brood box. Repeat the process with the other frames, making sure that you place them in the same sequence as they were in the nuc box. If you can spot the queen on a frame, take a little extra care moving it. You don't want her falling off and injuring herself.

Once you have transferred the frames, you'll find there are many bees still left at the bottom of the nuc box. Gently turn the box upside down and give it a good, firm jolt to shake the remaining bees out. Next, lean the nuc against the entrance of the hive: the stragglers will soon make their way in once they scent the bees already in there.

The next step is to close up the hive, very gently. Start by filling the spaces either side of the nuc frames with new frames and their foundation (see page 67). Depending on the type of hive you have, your brood frame will take either 10 or 12 frames in total. Put the cover or crown board on top, making sure there are no bees trapped around the edges. Use your beekeeper's brush to swish them away.

It's now time to give the bees their well-deserved supper of sugar solution. Fill the feeder – it will take about half of the quantity you have made up – and place it over the hole on the crown board. The roof of the hive won't fit on with the feeder in place, so you need to place an empty super on top of the brood box and then put the roof on.

Reduce the entrance to the hive to an opening of 2.5–5 cm (1–2 in) so the small colony can defend itself against intruders (including wasps who also happen to like sugar solution). Use your beekeeper's brush to brush off any stragglers attached to you – don't forget to check the back of your suit. Leave the bees to rest overnight. The next morning, remove the nuc box, which will now be empty of bees. Check the feeder and refill with the remaining sugar solution if needed.

MAKING INSPECTIONS

If the weather is warm, the bees have plenty of room and you don't disturb them too often, the colony will increase in size and become healthy and strong. Be content to watch your bees at a short distance for the first week. Foraging bees should be out flying and returning with pollen and nectar. Lots of pollen means a healthy laying queen with lots of brood to feed. Bees standing on the landing board beating their wings are wafting cool air into the hive to evaporate the water in the nectar to make honey. Don't be tempted to open the hive and look at them every day, they'll get fed up of being disturbed.

The first inspection

After nine days – that's the time it takes for the colony to cap its first batch of eggs – you can take a look at what's going on inside the hive. You want to see if the queen is laying, and that the worker bees have been cleaning up and repairing any leaking combs. As the grubs start to appear in the brood, you'll notice that your new frames are being moved into and the worker bees have been drawing out combs. This is a sign that the colony is on the increase and it will soon outgrow space in the brood box. Do your first inspection on a warm, sunny afternoon. Most of the worker bees will be out of the hive, which will give you a much clearer view of the frames. The warm weather also means the temperature inside the hive will not drop too dramatically.

Put on your bee-keeping suit, light your smoker and walk up to the hive slowly. Whenever possible approach the hive from the side or rear. If you go in at the front you will block the hive entrance, which will annoy the bees. Reach round and give the hive entrance a gentle puff or two of smoke. Wait for five minutes to allow the alarm to spread through the hive.

Lift off the roof of the hive. It should come away easily, but be prepared for the bees to have stuck it down with propolis. Have a look at the underside of the roof because there may well be some bees there. The queen bee is likely to be busy laying eggs in cells, but if she happens to be on the underside of the roof, you need to encourage her back into the darkness of the hive, which you can do by placing a corner of the roof over the hole in the crown board to get the queen down into the dark hole. Leave the roof on the ground near the hive, upside down so no bees are trapped underneath.

Remove the empty super housing the feeder and place that at the side of the hive. Take the feeder off the crown board – remember not to lose the plastic cup. If the feeder isn't empty you can replace it later after the inspection. Look down through the feeder hole in the crown board – you'll see bees! You can give a small puff of smoke here if you want, although this won't be necessary if the bees are happy and calm.

Remove the crown board. This will be stuck down with propolis, so run the sharp end of your hive tool all the way around the underside of the crown board to break the sticky seal and gently prise off the board. The more quietly and smoothly you work, the less chance the bees have of knowing that you're there. The underside of the crown board may have hundreds of bees on it – this is normal – so lean the crown board gently against the hive entrance.

You should examine each frame at this inspection: you're looking for eggs, larvae, sealed brood, pollen, honey and sealed honey. If the queen is marked you may catch sight of her, but don't worry if you don't. If you have eggs, larvae and sealed brood, she's in there somewhere!

Starting at one side of the hive, and using the curved end of your hive tool, gently lever the first frame out of position. Don't be alarmed if the frame still looks

brand new. This simply means that the bees haven't moved into this space yet. Most of the action takes place in the centre of the hive, where the bees maintain the brood nest in a sort of rugby ball shape, and it takes time to reach the outer edges of the frames.

Place the first frame inside the upturned lid of the hive on the ground. Now lever out the second frame, but slide it away from its neighbouring frame before lifting it out to avoid crushing any bees. Look at this frame and note any differences – this is where a tape recorder comes in handy, as you can speak your notes into it instead of taking time to write them down. The bees may have been drawing out wax and making new cells, or they may still be taking their time getting to this frame. Place this second frame in the box on the ground so you have a little more space to move the frames around in the hive. Keep releasing and sliding each frame away from the neighbouring one before you lift them out of the hive.

As you get closer to the centre of the brood and the five original nuc box frames there is much more activity. Look at the cells: some will be filled with liquid nectar and others with different coloured pollen. Some cells will be capped with white wax – these are the ones storing the honey – while others will have a darker

coloured wax containing the brood. You really want to see larvae at different stages of growth: the big, pearly coloured and 'C' shaped larvae are easy to spot. There should also be some cells with a tiny white egg in the bottom. To get the best view of what's happening inside each little chamber, stand with your back to the sun and hold the frame up in front of you so the light falls onto the cells. Where a frame has cells with eggs in them, there's a pretty good chance that the queen bee is also around. She can move quite quickly so look for her long body and legs and for her colour mark. If she is on that frame, take extra special care as you set the frame back so she is not damaged. Return the frame to its original position, making sure it faces the same way.

If your colony has been very busy, you may find that one side of the first and last frames has been drawn out. Check these frames carefully to make sure there is no brood in any of the cells: if all are clear, turn the frames around so the 'flat' side faces into the hive. This encourages the bees to draw out more cells and make the utmost use of all available space.

On all the frames, look carefully for the distinctive queen cells. These are the larger cells (about the size of acorns) that house princesses – the queens in waiting – and is a sign that the colony may be thinking of swarming (see pages 101–04).

Finishing the inspection

Once you have lifted out and checked all the frames, you need to return them to their original position in the hive. Gently put them back into place – it may be a bit of a squeeze! Use the hive tool to scrape off any comb and propolis from the crown board and place it back on top of the brood box, moving it gently from side to side as you replace it to avoid trapping and killing a lost bee. (A dying bee emits a scent that upsets other bees and causes them to become distressed and aggravated.)

If the weather has been fine and you have seen drawn out comb, nectar and pollen, you can remove the feeder even if there is some of the syrup still left over. Put the roof on (and secure the hive with its strap if fitted). If you are happy that the colony is doing well – there's plenty of larvae, capped brood and food – and the weather looks set to stay fair, open the hive entrance another 2.5–5 cm (1–2 in) to allow the bees more room to come and go and allow a bit more air to circulate.

Walk away from the hive and use your beekeeper's brush to remove any hitchhikers. Clean and put your kit away and get your notebook or record cards out. Record the date and time of the inspection; the weather; temperature; the mood of the bees; details of what you observed on each frame (amount of brood, amount of nectar and stored honey, queen cells); your actions, such as marking the queen, continuing to feed the bees with sugar solution, or removing the feeder; and whether you saw any pests or gave any medicine (this last must be recorded scrupulously). You also need to make a reminder note to tell you what you are going to do on the next inspection, such as adding a new super and frames. These records will help you understand the performance of each colony and you can use the information to improve the management of your bees.

Weekly inspections

You need to inspect the hive every seven days and should always record your findings. Remember that bees have to work really hard to maintain the temperature inside the hive at 35° C (95° F) so it's important that you don't chill the hive. Only enter the hive when the outside temperature is 15° C (59° F) and when it is not raining and when there is only a light wind. Carry out your weekly inspections in the late afternoon if possible, when most of the bees are out foraging and there are fewer of them in the hive.

THE EXPANDING COLONY

At some stage your bees will need more space as they fill the brood box frames with cells. Bees work vertically so, if you add a super too soon, they will just move into it leaving most of the frames in the brood box empty. You don't want this, because you want as many cells as possible available to the queen to lay in. This way, the bigger the colony, the more honey there will be to harvest, so make sure the frames on the ground floor are pretty fully occupied before adding a super extension. Adding supers is the first step in the management of your beehive (see page 92), but not before you have made up a new set of frames with foundation, all ready and waiting for the moment

BEE AND HIVE MANAGEMENT

The management of bees and the maintenance of the beehive consists of routine inspections carried out on a weekly basis throughout the season – generally from late April to early September. If the weather is warm enough, this can be extended from March to October, especially if there is a glut of ivy flowers that can provide late-season forage. Inspection is vital during May and June, and to a lesser extent in July, in order to prevent swarms. During these months it is vital that the queen cell is not overlooked. In the autumn, hive inspections can be less frequent – every two weeks or so. Remember that the outside temperature should ideally be 15° C (59° F) or above so that when you open the hive, there isn't a great rush of cold air that chills the bees and lowers the inside temperature too much. The bees will work hard to restore the hive temperature, and as you become more confident and competent, each inspection will take less time.

ADDING SUPERS

Once bees have settled into a new hive they start to get busy foraging. Inside the hive's brood box, they draw out new foundation on either side of the five original nuc frames to make extra storage space for the nectar, pollen and the thousands of eggs the queen is laying. At some stage, the space in the brood box will become full and you will have to add an extension – a super with new frames and foundation. Adding a super allows the bees to store honey outside of the brood box, freeing up space inside for the queen to lay more eggs.

When to add a super

Exactly when to add a super often depends on the weather: the finer the weather, the more pollen and nectar there is for the bees to collect and store in the hive. Weekly inspections help you to monitor the amount of space being filled in the brood box and the important thing to remember is that you need to add a super *before* you run out of space in the brood box. If the bees start to feel overcrowded, it triggers their natural instinct to swarm – something you don't want to happen in your first year with a new hive.

Each time you make an inspection you become more familiar with the workings of your hive and the space that the bees are filling up. This is where a digital camera helps, as you can refer to the previous inspection's images to help you make note of the progress. If the weather is good, you will see that your colony is expanding. When you take off the roof or lid and the crown board you'll be amazed at how busy and crowded the brood box looks, so make sure you have your super and frames prepared with foundation ready for the hive expansion.

Look carefully at the outermost frames in the brood box: a useful rule of thumb is that if the foundation has been drawn out by the bees into hexagonal tubes about 1 cm (2/3 in) then it's a good time to add a super.

Maintaining Your Beehive

Chapter **8**

How to add a super

Adding a super is very simple. It doesn't take long and it doesn't disturb the bees at all. In addition to the super and the frames, however, you will also need a queen excluder (see page 64). This is a wire mesh frame that sits on top of the brood box and stops the queen (and drones) entering and laying her eggs in the super. The mesh is big enough for worker bees to pass through, so they can still feed the queen and the brood.

Follow the procedure for a hive inspection (see page 88). Get appropriately dressed, have your smoker and hive tool ready, and approach the hive slowly and from the rear or side. Give a puff or two of smoke to the entrance and wait five minutes for the alarm signal to spread through the hive.

Lift the roof off the hive, take off the crown board and check carefully in case the queen is there. Place the crown board against the front of the hive so any bees on it will make their way into the hive to grab as much honey as they can carry and become a little too sleepy to be bothered to sting.

If there are lots of bees walking around on top of the brood frames, give them a puff of smoke to move them off. Now use your hive tool to scrape off any burr comb. This is the extra wax comb that may have accumulated on the top of the brood frames. This will ensure that the queen excluder lies nice and flat on top of the brood box.

Place the queen excluder on the brood box, making sure there are no bees trapped around the edges. Place the super on top of the queen excluder: the frames in the super should be aligned in the same way as those in the brood box – that is, either 'cold' or 'warm' (see page 80). Now replace the crown board and close the hive up again.

Brush off your suit, and clean your hive tool. Keep a record in your notebook of the date (and time if you wish) that you added the first super. You should also start to prepare new frames with foundation for your second super!

When to add a second super

When the season is really good, with lots of sunshine and warm weather, nectar flows even more abundantly. It is not unheard of in such conditions for bees to fill up the first super with honey. You should add a second super when the frames in the first super are half full. In a really good season – an early spring followed by a near perfect summer – you may find that you have to add as many as four supers to the hive to accommodate all that lovely honey.

You can add a second, and subsequent supers to a hive in two ways. First you can simply place the second super with its frames and foundation on top of the first super (known as top supering), which is very simple and quick to do. Alternatively you can bottom super. This is where you place the new super between the brood box and existing supers, which requires you to dismantle more of the hive. In your first year you should top super. The reason for this is because bees more readily accept super frames for storing honey that have already had their foundations drawn out: new foundation doesn't have drawn out cells and the bees have to make them

before they can store their nectar. In your first year of bee-keeping, all your foundations will have been new and clean. You won't have any drawn-out cells until you have harvested and spun off the honey from the frames of the first super. You can then use these drawn out frames for a subsequent super, and this is when you can bottom super if you wish to. On this occasion, because the bees in the brood box are much closer to the new empty super with drawn out cells, they don't have to spend time drawing out a new foundation and may well fill cells more quickly.

ENCOURAGING YOUR BEES

Sometimes, bees can seem a little bit hesitant about moving into a new super. If, on your weekly inspection, you find that they haven't been busy drawing out the foundation, you can remove the queen excluder to give them a bit more space to move around. At your next inspection, you should find that the bees have started to draw out the foundation, in which case you can replace the queen excluder. The scent they have marked the new super with will be now be familiar and will encourage the workers to pass through the queen excluder. Once the cells are filled with honey, they are capped in snowy white wax. You can leave this super in the hive until you are ready to harvest it (see pages 120–8) but make sure you have a new super, frames and foundation ready to add to the hive to provide more storage space.

FEEDING POLLEN

Bees do not live on nectar alone. In addition to a constant supply of fresh water near the hive, they also need pollen. Pollen is a bee's main source of protein, fat and vital minerals and it is estimated that to raise a single bee in the colony, 100mg of pollen is needed. The average colony will collect around 50 kg (110 lb) of pollen, the majority of which is used in rearing brood (the remainder is used to stimulate the bee's own hypopharyngeal gland).

The big problem for bees, however, is that pollen is not always regularly available. In a poor season, in some countries, it has been necessary to feed pollen substitutes made from a range of ingredients, such as fish meal, soya flour and egg yolk all mixed with sugar solution. The most important thing that beekeepers – and all gardeners – can do, is grow pollen-bearing plants throughout the year in window boxes, planters and hanging baskets, on roofs and balconies and in gardens. Encourage everyone around you to grow winter-flowering plants, vegetables and spring bulbs, fruit trees, summer and late season flowers and plants to ensure a ready supply of pollen to ensure the survival of your bees.

MOVING A HIVE

In the first season you may need to move the hive – out of a prevailing wind, for example. But bees always return to the same spot and if you move the hive more than 1 m (3 ft) away from its original spot, your bees will struggle to find it. The best approach, therefore, is to move a hive in short steps, just under one hive width each day. The best time of day to do this is at dusk or dawn, when the great majority of bees are safe inside the hive.

Moving a hive a greater distance – say you want your bees to take advantage of spring blossom in a nearby orchard or flowers in a local summer meadow – is not something that you should undertake until you have accumulated greater bee management skills. Even then, you'll need the help of an experienced beekeeper.

WEEKLY INSPECTIONS

Once your bees have made themselves at home and you have begun your weekly inspections, you will start to see differences each time you open the hive. Before lifting out any frames, look for brace comb. Looking down vertically between the frames, this is the wax that has been built between the frames to hold them together. Brace comb does not contain any grubs so it's safe for you to separate the frames by sliding a knife between the frames.

Burr comb

The base of the frames is often stuck with propolis and you will often find some burr comb – extraneous wax – drawn around the base. Use your hive tool to scrape this away and remove any burr comb on the top of the bars as well. If your hive tool meets any resistance on the bottom of frames, go gently as this is likely to be one of the pins holding the frame bars together or one of the wire loops holding the foundation in place. When it comes to inspecting frames in the brood box, you'll need to work carefully when cleaning them, because you don't want to damage or tear open any of the cells that contain grubs.

Egg cells

Look carefully at each frame. Find the brood areas with eggs and grubs and capped cells, and search the outer cells for honey and pollen. Finding cells containing eggs tells you that the queen is laying. If you examine the position of each egg in the cell, you'll be able to tell when the queen was last laying on a particular frame. Day-old eggs are glued vertically to the base of the cell. By day two, the eggs will have fallen over to lie at 45 degrees. On the third day, the eggs lie flat on the bottom of the cell.

A queen that is laying well lays her eggs in the warmest part of the frame – usually starting in the centre and spreading outwards. Her first workings on a new frame will be in the centre and these will be capped first by the worker bees. In a circle around this, you are likely to see uncapped brood. These cells in turn are likely to be surrounded by cells filled with store, first pollen and then honey, set as arches around the brood. (If you have a polystyrene hive, the queen will lay right up to the edge of the brood frame, because the walls of the hive offer extra insulation.)

Queen cells

When you undertake your general inspection of the frames, it's vital that you look out for the larger queen cells. This is where queens-in-waiting are reared. These queen cells are pretty easy to identify: they are bigger – usually 2.5 cm (1 in) long – elongated cells that look a bit like a peanut shell and hang vertically from the comb.

Queen cells can be found in two locations: in the middle of a frame and/or hanging from the bottom of a frame. Cells located in the middle of a frame indicate that the queen is sick and not laying well, because this is where cells are made in an emergency. Cells hanging from the bottom of a frame indicate either that the queen is failing or that the hive is overcrowded. The presence of queen cells in late spring is a sign that the colony is getting ready to swarm.

If you know that your queen is less than two years old and healthy, you should remove any queen cells that you find. If there are no competing unmated queens around, the colony is much less likely to swarm. If you are uncertain about the age or the health of the queen, contact an experienced beekeeper, who will be able to help you.

SWARMING

Here is a useful point at which to understand why bees swarm and what you can do to prevent it. There is often no real reason why a perfectly healthy colony with a fit, young, laying queen and plenty of space should want to vacate the hive, except for the fact that swarming is a natural part of a honeybee's life cycle. In doing so, bees not only produce more colonies but exchange genetic material that allows them to evolve. As outlined above, you can take steps to prevent a swarm if your queen is under two years old, is healthy and laying. The first is to remove queen cells (a colony will swarm when it has reared a number of virgin queens to take over the hive). The second is to add supers and a second brood box so there's more living room.

You can also clip one of the queen's wings. This prevents her from flying too far from the hive so the rest of the colony won't wander far either. This is a delicate operation and you may want expert help from a more experienced beekeeper for this. Also, now that the queen has limited flight, she can often get trampled on in a swarm and this makes her very vulnerable to injury or death.

Cast swarms

When a colony swarms, it leaves around half of its bees in the hive, along with brood at all stages of development and a new queen in the making. To ensure there is a new queen, the worker bees have prepared and looked after enough cells to ensure a succession: there may be up to 12 new queens in waiting. Nine days after being capped over, the virgins emerge. This is usually when the swarm leaves the colony with the old queen.

The first new virgin queen to emerge after the swarm has left may now decide to have her own swarm, called a cast swarm. She also leaves, with about half the remaining colony, and looks for a new home. The remaining colony has now been reduced in numbers to about one-quarter of its original size. The next queen to emerge may also cast swarm, and the whole process can be repeated until the hive is completely empty. You can prevent this once the first new queen has emerged by destroying any remaining queen cells in the hive.

Catching and throwing a swarm

When a swarm of bees leaves the hive, it usually happens before midday on a nice day in late spring or early summer. They leave the hive and fly around haphazardly for around 20 minutes or so before forming into a thick black buzzing cloud and settling temporarily on a tree branch or fence post located within 50 m (54 yd) of the hive. Here, they form themselves into a rugby-ball-shaped mass around the queen and wait for anything between an hour and a day until returning scout bees communicate that they have sourced a suitable new home. The bees gorge on enough honey to keep them going for three days. This is your opportunity to get the bees away from their temporary spot and into a nice newly prepared brood box.

This is best done with someone helping you. Once ready, give the branch they are on a short, sharp, shake so that you and your helper can catch the ball of bees in a skep or an open cardboard box. If the bees are on a fence post, use your bee-keeper's brush gently to nudge them in. If you have to get them upwards into the box, you could try giving a short puff of smoke from below to encourage them.

Once you have the bees in the box, cover it with a white bed sheet and take them to their new brood box home. The bees' instinct is to follow the scouts and the queen, so you need to encourage them into the hive using a procedure known as 'throwing a swarm'. Position a piece of board (about 120 x 60 cm/4 x 2ft) leaning against the landing board so that it slopes down to the ground. Place the box of bees at the foot of the ramp and cover the ramp with the white bed sheet. Make sure the sheet and board are touching the hive entrance, but not blocking it. Turn the box out and dump the bees on the sheet. The bees will crawl up the sheet, through the entrance and into the darkness of their new brood box home. Once the queen is in, the rest of the swarm follows. What you have basi-cally done is tricked the bees into thinking they have found their new home on their own, which means they are much quicker and happier to settle in.

If a bed sheet is unavailable or time is pressing, you can turn the box upside down over the new brood box complete with its frames. Put the roof on the hive and leave the box near the hive entrance. As the bees inside the new hive waft their scent around, any bees still outside will soon be able to locate their mates and join them. You now have a second colony of bees that you can either keep or pass on to another beekeeper. If you keep the swarm, note that it will expand very quickly, so you'll need to be ready to add a super and frames to accommo-date the newcomers.

Preventing a swarm

If, when you inspect a hive, there are queen cells with larvae in them, you know the colony is preparing to swarm, and that they will do so as soon as the queen cell is capped. It takes five and a half days for an egg to develop into larva, so time is on your side. The best way to prevent a swarm is by splitting the colony in two, so tricking the bees into thinking that they have swarmed already. One way of doing this is to create a nuc (see page 81).

You will need a nuc box, or spare brood box, with five brood frames, a floor and a cover board. Start by looking through the hive for a frame with pollen and honey. Place this and any bees on it into the nuc box. Next, find the queen and the frame she is on and place this (and her) into the nuc box. This frame should have brood at all stages of development on it. If you see any queen cells, remove them. Find another frame full of pollen and honey, remove any queen cells and place this in the nuc box. You need more bees, so brush the bees off two further frames in the hive and into the nuc box. Fill the remaining space with empty frames with foundation. Close up the nuc box and place it on a new stand at least 1 m (3 ft) away from the original hive.

Returning to the original hive, destroy any queen cells that are about to be capped, leaving just a few queen cells that have young larvae in them. Slide the remaining frames together towards the centre of the hive and fill up the side spaces with new frames and foundation and close the hive. You now have the original hive with no queen but some developing queen cells, and a nuc box with the old queen, some developing brood, some nurse bees and some food stores.

After a week, go back to the original hive and destroy all but one of the capped queen cells. It's a good idea to remove the frame with the first queen cell you find and place it safely to one side and then destroy all the remaining queen cells. When you are left with only one queen cell, place the frame back in the hive, close up and leave it for four weeks, after which time, you should have a newly mated queen who has started laying. Don't open the hive any sooner than four weeks, as virgins and newly mated queens are quite nervous and don't like being disturbed.

In the meantime, you can build the bees in the nuc into a new colony with the old queen, or you can remove the old queen and reunite the bees as one colony in the old hive with their new queen once she is nicely settled.

A FAILING QUEEN

It's likely, in your first season as a beekeeper with a young healthy queen, that any queen cells you find are at the frame bottoms, so indicating a need for extra space in the hive rather than any sickness on the part of the queen. However, it is worth knowing how to spot a failing queen.

Remember that the queen lays in the warmest part of a frame – starting in the centre and working outwards. A failing queen does not lay in this uniform manner. On your inspection you may see cells that have eggs in them that are not viable, and that capped brood cells have little holes in them where the queen has 'missed'. When cells look patchy and weak, it's a sign that the colony is in danger of a reduction in numbers of new bees being born. Worker bees will now start the process of replacing the ailing queen in a process known as supersedure.

Supersedure and re-queening

The process of removing an old queen and replacing her with a new one is called supersedure. It's a natural process, although beekeepers tend to re-queen every two years to ensure the hive remains vigorous, because a young queen's laying rate is high. Re-queening also reduces the likelihood of a colony swarming.

Natural supersedure is when a young queen develops into a mature, but virgin, queen bee, which generally sets the old queen off out of the hive, taking a swarm with her (see page 102). Beekeepers avoid this swarm by killing the old queen and removing all the queen cells except one. A week or so later, the new queen emerges, by which time the colony has come to accept her. She mates with drones and begins her work laying eggs. One method of dispatching an old queen for a forced supersedure entails amputating one of her rear legs. This stops her from correctly positioning her eggs and sends a signal to the worker bees that something is wrong. They then start to build queen cells and kill the old queen by 'balling' her: a number of worker bees attach themselves to the old queen and increase their body temperature until she dies from heat exhaustion. Because an injury to the queen can set the supersedure process in motion, extra care must be taken by a beekeeper when opening and closing the hive.

An alternative to raising a new queen in the hive is to add a replacement queen (she can be purchased or reared in another hive) who is introduced to the colony by placing her in a queen cage. This keeps her safe from attack and damage while the rest of the hive get used to her scent and accept her.

Regardless of the method of supersedure, it's important that it takes place when there are enough male drones around to inseminate a new queen. This is usually in the late autumn or the earlier part of winter.

PREPARING FOR WINTER

Late summer marks the end of a bee's year, but not a beekeeper's, because there is still plenty to do to ensure the survival of the colony over the long winter ahead. The amount of nectar available for the bees to gather will have fallen off, so the hard-working female worker bees evict the male drones from the hive. The queen reduces her laying activity and the brood nest shrinks to just a few frames. The beekeeper will have removed honey supers for harvesting (see page 120), so the hive height will also have been reduced to brood box height. Around 10,000 of the bees will live out the winter in the single brood box, huddled together to keep warm and feeding off their supply of stored honey.

The beekeeper's tasks now involve making sure the hive stays safe and watertight, vermin proof and ventilated. Fallen leaves need to be swept clear of the roof to avoid blocking vital ventilation holes. Similarly, a blanket of snow on a hive blocks ventilation holes, while melt water can enter the hive. You can tilt the hive forward a little bit – 2.5 cm (1 in) wooden blocks positioned underneath the back legs of the hive stand will work – so that any rainwater runs off cleanly. If your hive is in a sheltered spot, you can pop a matchstick under a corner of the crown board just to open it up a crack to increase ventilation without causing a draught. Wait until the weather is colder to do this, as the bees will be clustered together in the brood box and won't break away to seal up the gap with propolis. Cut back any grass or plants around the hive to avoid dampness. If it's windy, make sure the hive is battened down with a securing strap or weighed down with a nice, large rounded stone.

The hive entrance needs to be kept open a little so the bees can come and go to defecate, so make sure snow does not block the hive entrance and keep the landing board clear so they don't bring snow or wet into the hive on their hairy legs and bodies.

Well before the bees bed down for the winter, they need to have a good feed. This is to compensate for the honey you have taken. Throughout the winter it is also important that due care is given to pest control to avoid the remaining colony becoming weakened by disease (see pages 130–7).

Autumn feeding

Bees 'dry out' nectar in order to turn it into honey. They beat their wings to produce the currents of air needed to evaporate the water in the nectar. They do the same thing to the sugar-syrup feed that you provide them with. This means that their big feed before winter should be given in the autumn, while the weather is still warm enough to help evaporate the water in the solution. Even if there is a glorious Indian summer, and it's still warm and dry, make sure your bees have a good feed as soon as you've finished your last honey harvest, because they won't be able to process and store food fast enough to keep through the winter if it suddenly turns cold.

How much feed?

The average colony needs around 18 kg (40 lb) of stores to see it through the winter. This means that you need to assess how much honey is left in the hive. A standard National hive brood frame holds a little over 2 kg (about 5 lb) of honey. At this time of the year, it's likely that the four outer brood frames are full of honey and the remaining frames contain a mixture of brood, pollen and stored honey. Four frames of honey therefore hold in total 8 kg (about 17 1/2 lb) of honey – less than half it needs to survive. It is down to you to provide them with the rest –10 kg (22 1/2 lb) of sugar.

The solution is made in two strengths (see page 86). White granulated sugar is always used, because there is some evidence that unrefined or brown sugar can cause dysentery in bees. Because the sugar solution is odourless, you can make it a little more tempting to the bees by adding some honey. (Do not feed your bees honey unless you are certain of its origin: imported honey can contain nosema and foulbrood spores). Measure the water first, bring it to a rolling boil, add the honey until it is dissolved, and then make up the solution with the appropriate amount of sugar.

Bees rob each other's hives of stores and if it obvious that there is sugar in a hive, this can exacerbate the problem. The bees indicate this by flying around in a highly excited manner and communicating the presence of sugar to bees from other hives. To reduce the likelihood of robbing, it's a good idea to do any feeding (or topping up of feeders) at dusk. If robbing persists, close the hive entrance up a little so the home colony can defend it more easily. Do not spill or dribble sugar solution on the outside of the hive, as this will encourage bees and wasps to come.

Autumn feed solution is made with one part water to one part sugar. Circular feeders hold about 1 l (2 pt) of solution, so you'll have to refill it several times over. A colony of bees at this time of year can consume this amount in just 48 hours if they need nourishment, so you'll need to be ready with plenty more sugar solution when they've used up their first batch. Don't worry about over-feeding: bees only take as much as they can use, transform and store in all the available cells. Once they stop taking the solution, you can remove the feeder.

Adding medicine to the feed

With this feed comes a good opportunity to medicate and treat the bees for nosema (see page 133). You can add the antibiotic medication to the sugar solution following the manufacturer's instructions. You must make a note of the dates and the medication given on your Medicines Record Card (including the manufacturer's batch numbers for later reference). Going into the winter with healthy bees and a strong honey store will also keep nosema down and ensure a healthy colony re-emerges in spring.

INTRUDERS

In the winter, mice are on the hunt for a cosy, warm place to bed down and a hive is the perfect spot. You need to reduce the size of the entrance to the hive, because mice can get through very small holes. The most effective way of doing this is to buy a mouse guard. This is essentially a strip of galvanised metal with two rows of 10 mm (1/2 in) holes punched through, which you fasten over the entrance of the hive. The holes are big enough for bees to pass through – remember they need access at all times – but hopefully small enough to keep mice out. If you live in an area where badgers, skunks and raccoons are common, you need to make an enclosure for the hive with some wire mesh screens to keep them out. If there are bears in your woods, then you need electric fencing.

INSIDE A HIVE IN AUTUMN

Now that the size of a colony has shrunk to around 10,000 bees – a cluster that's large enough to keep the temperature in the hive at the right level, but small enough to survive on the honey stores – the queen takes a rest from laying, and will not begin again until shortly after the winter solstice.

The bees take turns to cluster around the queen to keep her warm and then move to the colder outer edges of the cluster to feed on stores. Many of the worker bees are born in the autumn and survive the winter to start the work of the new season. There are, nonetheless, deaths. The bodies of bees that don't survive are dragged out of the hive and deposited on the ground. You should tidy these away. Bees must have access to the outside at all times, and on a cold but dry day, you will see bees taking a short trip out to relieve themselves. They may also gather a bit of pollen if there is any about. Watching hive entrance activity is part of a beekeeper's autumn duty. Seeing bees with pollen is a good sign that the queen is still laying eggs and that larvae are being fed. If all is right with the colony, the bees work their way through their honey stores and, as winter draws to a close, start to rebuild the colony as spring returns.

Autumn checklist

As the temperature begins to fall and the days shorten, you can limit hive inspections to once every two weeks and expect to see a decrease in the number of bees in the brood. Now is the time to:

- Remove the supers from the hive, clean and dry them.
- Feed the bees.
- Test and treat for varroa (see page 132).
- Fit a mouse guard over the hive entrance.
- Keep an eye open for wasps and robber bees who will steal the honey stores designed for the colony.
- Watch for wax moth infestation (see page 137).
- Keep the water supply fresh.

In mid-autumn, before closing the hive for the last time, make one final thorough inspection

- Make sure all the parts of the hive fit snugly together to keep out draughts and so the bees do not have to use vital energy filling up spaces with propolis.
- If you have a WBC hive (see page 59), check under the gabled roof care fully to make sure there's nothing making a winter nest in there.

In late autumn, you will have stopped feeding the bees. All the combs occupied by the bees should have at least two-thirds of the cells filled and capped by the end of September/beginning of October. If this is not the case, you should give the bees an extra feed straight away.

Now is the time to make sure that the hive is fully secured and can withstand the worst weather:

- Make sure the hive cover fits tightly and, if necessary, make it a tighter fit by fitting a sheet of clear plastic or a cloth of natural fibre over the hive top. The flight entrance will provide enough ventilation.
- Cover hives left outdoors in roofing paper weighed down with some wooden battens secured by rocks.
- Clear away the bodies of ejected drones.

Do not disturb the hive too much – you want the bees to have sealed any gaps with propolis to keep draughts out.

A HIVE IN WINTER

In winter, the hive is 'asleep' but there are still plenty of activities for a beekeeper to undertake. Early winter is a good time to make a start on catching up and organising your records, making sure that you have noted any medicinal treatments and doing some more reading on bee culture and bee-keeping.

You will continue to make visual inspections of the hive, but you must never open the hive. Instead check for any storm damage and that the mouse guard is still in place.

- Work near the hive quietly, without making any banging noises to disturb the bees. Remove any dead bees at the entrance.
- Brush away any snow from the entrance and from the ground in front of the hive. Bees will fly on dry days in winter but if there is snow on the ground, they can become confused by the extra ultraviolet light. You can also erect a shade over the entrance to help cut down on this.
- Look for bees flying on warmer days and observe their vitality.
- Check and clean all your equipment.
- Construct new frames with foundation ready for the new season.
- Consider investing in a new, second hive. You may now have decided to expand your apiary, and you'll need a second hive in order to house a swarm in spring.
- Make sure the bees have access to a supply of fresh, unfrozen water at all times.

In the late winter, as winter-flowering bulbs come into bloom, you may start to see increased activity as the bees start to gather some of the newly available pollen and the queen starts to lay again. This can be a difficult time for the bees but it is important that you do not open the hive. If you are worried that they are starving, contact an experienced beekeeper for advice. He or she may suggest a winter feed of candy. This gives the bees an energy boost, although they cannot store the food for later use. Some beekeepers advocate a candy feed only in early spring, when there are meagre food supplies in the hive. You can buy blocks of bee candy from bee suppliers. Wrap a piece in greaseproof paper, make a hole in the underside of the paper and place the candy block (hole side down) on top of the feeding hole in the crown board, leaving enough room for ventilation. The bees come up through the hole to eat the candy.

A HIVE IN SPRING

Early spring may bring forth some blossom at a very welcome time for the bees, but the weather is still very variable. A warm spell may encourage the bees to increase the size of the colony, but if this is followed by a cold or wet spell, and the bees can't forage, they have to rely on their already diminished stores to feed the increasing numbers of brood and young bees. This inevitably puts a strain on the bees and is when they are most likely to run out of food. Keep an eye on the weather and be prepared to offer a feed of sugar solution (see page 134). If the weather is set to stay bad make a strong solution and be prepared to refill the feeder.

The first warm spring day

When this day arrives, you can take your first look of the year in the hive to see what's what. But before you open the hive:

*   Check the entrance. This tells you plenty about what's happening inside. Bees arriving with pollen means the queen is laying.
*   Look for signs of diarrhoea. Lines of brown deposits about 2.5 cm (1 in) long on the landing board and hive walls. This may be due to dampness or nosema (see page 134).
*   Gently, put your ear against a wall of a hive and listen for a healthy buzzing.

Take off the lid and crown board for a brief moment to avoid chilling the bees. Do this only on a nice warm day. Ideally, the outside temperature should be around 15° C (59° F).

The spring clean: stage 1

Once the weather is warm enough, you can start to give the hive a spring clean and replace the old brood comb with fresh comb. This reduces both the risk of disease and swarming. A complete spring clean takes a month, carried out in three visits of about half an hour each.

On a nice warm day, in the afternoon when all the foraging bees are out of the hive, you can make the first cleaning trip to the hive.

You need:
- A new brood box filled with frames and foundation
- A feeder with a strong sugar solution
- A new (or cleaned) crown board
- A new (or cleaned) varroa mesh floor
- A new (or cleaned) entrance block

Put on your bee-keeping suit and light your smoker. Approach the hive quietly from the side or rear taking care not to cast a shadow over the entrance. Give the hive entrance a few light puffs of smoke and wait for a couple of minutes before you open up.

Inside the hive you should be able to see:
- Bees occupying four or five frames – not necessarily in the middle of the brood box – with brood in them and nurse bees attending to the larvae.
- The remaining empty or near empty frames – these are the ones you want to remove.

You need to replicate the bees' natural method of keeping their nest nice and clean by migrating upwards into a nice new brood box, leaving the old one behind. Start at the end of the hive furthest away from the mass of bees and look at the first frame. If it is empty or has just a few cells of capped honey, take it out and place it to one side. Carry on until you come to a frame that has pollen on one side and (most likely) brood on the other. Return this to its exact same position, but in the new brood box.

Move to the opposite side of the hive and repeat the process of removing empty frames until you reach a frame with pollen and brood. You should end up with about four or five frames with pollen, brood and bees in the new box. If you need to, slide the frames together into the centre of the brood box and return to the box any frames that had a good supply of honey (perhaps two frames will be full of honey) so there are now six or seven frames in the centre of the new brood box.

Set this new brood box on top of the old brood box. Make sure all the frames face the same way in both boxes. Put on the feeder and fill it up with sugar solution – drip a little into the hive to let the bees know it's there – and close up the hive. Top up the feeder over the next two weeks, to give the bees extra energy to draw out the new foundation.

The spring clean: stage 2

Once the bees have begun to draw out the new foundation, the queen should move into the nice new brood box and start laying there. Take a look in the top brood box after a week to see if this is happening. If it is, introduce the queen excluder between the two brood boxes to keep the queen in the top brood box, while the workers pass to and fro. If she isn't there yet, encourage her with a puff or two of smoke at the hive entrance. If this doesn't work, then you need to find her and carefully, but manually, place her in her new home. Her attendant bees will soon follow, along with the workers.

The spring clean: stage 3

Twenty-one days after the queen has moved into the upper brood box, the brood that she laid in the lower box will have hatched and you can move on to the third, and final, stage of the spring clean.

This time, you need to:

- Remove the old brood box and frames
- Replace the old floor with a new (or cleaned) varroa mesh floor
- Replace the crown board with a new (or cleaned) one
- Replace the entrance block with a new (or cleaned) one

You can reuse the old brood box after cleaning and scorching it to remove any infestations, but should dispose of the old frames in case they harbour any disease in their joints. You can melt down any wax on them for later use.

In late spring

The colony should be growing by now, but may still need additional feeding with sugar solution. On your, now weekly, inspections, check the food stores the bees have accumulated. When they no longer require the feeder, you can remove it.

You now need to keep a close eye on the new brood box to make sure the bees don't run out of space. Once the spring blossom is fully out and the nectar starts to flow well, the brood will expand very rapidly. If the bees start to get overcrowded they will instinctively prepare to swarm, so keep a close look out for queen cells and be ready with a second 'bait' hive available (see page 102) or ready to add the first super (see page 93). The frames in this, and subsequent supers, should be the ones you removed at the end of the previous season for the honey harvest (see page 124).

If you used an extractor to harvest your honey, the frames will have the drawn out honeycombs intact, so the bees can get straight to work filling them with nectar. If you didn't use an extractor and had to scrape off the frames to harvest, you need to replace the foundation for the bees to draw out anew.

This is also the time to consider the age and health of your queen. If she is now older than two years, you may want to consider re-queening (see page 104). Depending on her age and health you can consider removing the queen cells (see page 101), or supersedure (see page 105).

A SUMMER HIVE

This is the time when your bees are at their busiest making honey. Make sure you are ready with extra supers and frames to accommodate them. Early summer is also when you should move the central frames in the brood box to the outside edges of the box. In a laying cycle of 21–22 days, these will have emptied and can be replaced with new frames. You can reuse old frames but they must be thoroughly cleaned – preferably by freezing them – or you can harvest the wax and make new foundation.

A healthy young queen will be at the peak of her laying now, so on your weekly hive inspection you should:

- Look for busy worker bees tending eggs and grubs and plenty of capped brood.
- See whether or not the bees are getting close to needing more room.
- Check on the queen every week.
- Be vigilant about swarming.
- Check for varroa.

By mid-summer, although the threat of swarming has passed, you should still remain vigilant. By this time you can add an extra super and frames, which you will later rob for the honey. Your weekly inspections continue and are always recorded in your notebook or record cards and you will be:

- Checking regularly for any signs of varroa infestation.
- Checking the health of the queen, especially if she is two years old.
- Adding an extra super (only if it is evident that the bees are capping the cells in the lower super).
- Preparing to extract honey.

Late summer is harvest time and you can begin by removing the supers and frames laden with honey. You must, however, make sure that the colony is left with at least 18 kg (40 lb) of honey for their own supply – or be ready to compensate them by feeding them (see page 107).

At this time of the year, you should still make your weekly inspections and you will be:

- Removing supers and frames to har vest honey, reducing the overall height of the hive.
- Feeding the bees to compensate them for the honey you have robbed and allow them to re-build their store for winter.
- Removing wax and rendering it, to gether with any burr wax accumulated through the year on hive inspections.
- Cleaning and replacing dirty frames.
- Closing the entrance to the hive by about 5 cm (2 in) so the bees can with stand any wasp intrusions.

Soon it will be autumn and the hive needs to be prepared for the oncoming winter. In the meantime, you have your second year's harvest of honey to extract.

Chapter **9**

Harvesting
Honey

THE HARVEST

A well-managed hive can produce honey that is in excess of the bees' needs, which leaves the beekeeper free to harvest it. It's important to remember though, that when you do harvest honey from a hive, you need to compensate the bees for their loss by substituting the equivalent weight in sugar solution. A careful beekeeper won't take more than the colony can afford to lose.

How much honey?

The amount of honey you can expect from a single hive in your first year varies between 9 and 18 kg (20 and 40 lb). The variation is down to a number of factors including, of course, the weather. The availability of good forage, how many other hives there are in the neighbourhood that are competing for this forage, the health of the bees, and how you have managed the hive – adding supers to make more space for honey – all contribute to the final tally. From season to season amounts vary, and this is where scrupulous record keeping helps because it allows you to see exactly what the optimum conditions were one year so you can better manage the hive the next.

When to harvest

The timing of your harvest also depends on a number of factors, the most important being which type and density of flowers, crops and trees are growing within a 5 km (3 mile) radius of your hive. Again the weather is a factor here. You may find that by midsummer, a honey super (or two) is full. If there is a long summer, you may find that you have a second harvest towards the end of it.

There are no guarantees, however. Even two hives in the same garden will produce different quantities of honey over different times. This is why you need to make weekly inspections through the main season. Also hard to predict, is what your honey will taste like, unless the hives are close enough to a particularly rich source of nectar.

OILSEED RAPE

Increasingly, farmers have planted fields of oilseed rape. Bees love the bright yellow flowers and its nectar is available in spring so they can get at it quite early. You may find you have a super full of oilseed rape honey by late spring, and this can be a bit of a problem. Apart from being pale yellow and pretty bland-tasting, honey made from oilseed rape pollen crystallises on the frames very quickly so that bees can't use it to feed themselves or their brood. If you know there are fields of this crop nearby and you have a super full of pale yellow, medium thick honey by late spring, you must remove it immediately.

The honey you harvest is likely to be that contained in the top-most super, or supers if you're really lucky. Always leave one full super of honey for the bees' winter store. Removing one full super to make way for a feeder set on the crown board allows you to top up the feeder quickly. And because you don't need to open the hive to do this, the bees stay nice and warm in their hive with no cold draughts.

Preparation

Ideally you need a large space, indoors, well away from the hive so that the bees (and wasps) can't smell it. The plan is to get the honey out of the frames and into containers without bits of wax in it. To get the honey out of the supers, you have to get rid of the bees on the frames. Set the super containing the honey frames on the crown board with a Porter bee escape in the hole (see page 65). The bees can enter the hive through this, but can't exit through the valve, so have to go out by the hive entrance. Put the roof back on the hive and wait a day at least before opening the hive. By this time, the bees should have moved 'downstairs' and the super for harvesting should be pretty bee-free.

When you return to the hive, you need to act quickly, but smoothly. Take the roof or lid off the hive and remove the super. Watch out, because it will be very heavy. Take it well away from the hive. Take off the Porter bee escape, set the feeder over the hole in the crown board and put the roof or lid back on.

In spite of the bee valve, there will inevitably be some bees on the frames inside the super. Remove them carefully so they can return to the hive. Once each frame is cleared of bees, place it in a large, clear-plastic, sealable box for safekeeping. This will allow you to carry all the frames into your harvesting room without bees following you.

TAKING THE HONEY
OFF THE FRAME

Getting the honey off the frames is a sticky business. It also takes a bit of time, so make sure you can work somewhere out of the way of others. Your equipment and working area needs to be sterile, and the windows and doors shut so bees and wasps can't fly in. You'll also need a fair bit of equipment to remove the capping, extract the honey and process the honey – honey knives, extractors, filters and plenty of sterile jars and lids. If you are a member of a bee-keeping club, it's often possible to do your honey extracting on their premises, which saves energy and money, particularly as extractors can be expensive.

Jars used for storing honey are usually ones that hold around 455 g (1 lb). Be wary of using washed and sterilised jars that stored other foodstuffs previously: odours and flavours can linger and honey is very good at absorbing these. Old jars that once held pickles or anything in vinegar or with garlic should be avoided completely. Furthermore, honey is hydroscopic – it draws water from the atmosphere – so all jars used must be sealable. Drawn in water can lead to fermentation and subsequent spoiling. Your local bee club or bee-keeping supplier will most likely have a selection of new jars available and ready for the harvest season.

There are a number of ways in which you can collect honey and it depends on the range of equipment you have. Once you have your frames safely inside, you need to decide whether you want some comb honey (see below), or whether you want to extract all the honey from the combs as liquid honey. You can, of course, have both.

Comb honey

To make comb honey, all you have to do is take a thin, very sharp knife and slice some chunks of comb – say about 10 x 7.5 cm (4 x 3 in) straight from the frames. If you have been using a wired foundation, you need to cut the wire and pull it out of the comb before putting it into a container. You can then place this chunk of comb in a jar and fill it up with liquid honey.

Scraping off honey

If you don't have access to an extractor (see below), you can still harvest plenty of honey by scraping the comb manually. This takes longer and is really sticky, but does have the advantage that fewer air bubbles get trapped in the honey. The downside of scraping the comb is that it destroys the honeycomb, as, ideally, you want to keep the drawn-out comb on the frames and give it back to the bees. Doing this means that they don't have to go through all the hard work of drawing out a clean, flat foundation but instead get straight on with the work of filling and capping the cells with new nectar.

To scrape the combs of honey, you'll need:

- A big clean pot to collect the honey
- A large clean container for the comb
- A large spoon or scraper
- A coarse sieve
- A fine sieve
- Another large pot or honey bucket with a lid and, ideally, a honey gate (a valve and tap at the bottom) through which the honey can flow smoothly and slowly
- Sealable jars

Start by placing the coarse sieve over the large pot and hold the frame with the honeycomb over it. Scrape the honey straight off the frame, comb and all, into the sieve. You won't be able to use that foundation again, so you can scrape as hard as you like.

In the sieve will be a lovely mass of comb and honey. Leave it as it is to allow the honey to drip through the sieve into the pot below. Once most of the honey has passed through, empty the wax comb scrapings into the other pot or container. You'll be able to give this a second sieving and use the leftover beeswax for making candles, polish, skin-care ointments – whatever takes your fancy. Continue scraping all the frames until they are empty.

To get beautifully clean honey, you now have to use the finer sieve to catch any small bits of wax and pollen. You can use a piece of muslin if you can hold it in place. One method is to tie the corners of a large square of muslin to the upturned legs of a kitchen stool, with the collecting bowl placed directly underneath, resting on the underside of the seat.

When the second sieving is complete, put a lid on the container or bucket and let the honey stand so any air bubbles rise to the surface. This can take a couple of days to complete, because it all depends on the consistency of the honey and the ambient temperature. The great thing about using a honey bucket with a honey gate is that when all the air bubbles have gone, you can open the gate and fill up individual jars cleanly and quickly.

You can return the empty frames to the super from which they came. They will be sticky, but this does not matter. Place the super above the crown board in the hive, making sure the hole in it is open. In a few days' time, you'll find the frames have been licked clean by those busy bees and you can now put new foundation in.

Using an extractor

An extractor speeds up the harvesting process – and cuts down on sticky spills – but it is expensive. Powered versions cost the most, but there are also manual versions available, if you're prepared to give your arms a workout. Your bee-keeping club may well have a powered extractor for members' use, but be prepared to queue at busy times.

Extractors use centrifugal force to remove the honey from the frames. You slice off the cappings of the comb on each side of a frame using a heated knife and place up to four frames (for a small extractor) into the drum. This spins (slowly at first, to avoid breaking the comb) and throws the liquid honey against the walls of the tank, where it runs down the sides into a collecting reservoir below.

Gradually increase the speed to extract as much honey as possible and turn the frames around to make sure both sides are harvested (bigger radial extractors do both sides at once). When no more honey comes off the frames and the force needed to spin the frames is lighter, remove the frames and return them to the super, where the bees will lick off any remaining honey. Because the extractor leaves the comb intact, the bees have cells already drawn out, waiting to be filled with nectar.

An extractor's reservoir has a coarse filter that removes any bits of wax and the honey is then transferred to a second holding vessel to rest for 24 hours, allowing the bubbles of air to rise to the surface and break. A second filtering (into a honey bucket, as above) follows and it takes around half an hour to sieve 9 kg (20 lb) of honey – about one full super's worth. The honey is then left to settle in the honey bucket for a further 24 hours before being poured into jars.

The cappings that you removed are, themselves, full of honey. You can put them in a sieve in a warm place and let the honey drip through into a collecting pot before using the wax. If you wash the wax in plenty of clean water, any remaining stickiness and sweetness will be removed.

POURING HONEY INTO JARS

Once the honey has rested for 24 hours, it should be poured into jars. Don't do it any sooner than this, as you don't want air bubbles in it. While air bubbles don't affect the flavour of the honey, at some stage they will rise to the surface and form an unsightly scum or foam on the honey.

While pouring, the honey bucket's gate is designed to ensure minimum contact with the air as the honey is let off and so reduces the risk of introducing new air bubbles. If your container doesn't have a valve or gate, then don an apron and roll up your sleeves, because the only way of getting honey out of the bucket and into jars is to decant it using a jug. As soon as a jar is full of honey, seal it with a lid.

Label each jar of honey with the location of the hive, the month and the year the honey was made. Store the jars in a dark cupboard or larder at room temperature.

EXPANDING

You'll be mightily impressed by your first season's crop and this may lead you to think about growing your apiary. You may even think about keeping bees not only for pleasure but for profit. A few jars sold at the village fête or at a farmers' market won't take too much trouble. Legally, however, you should inform the Inland Revenue and make sure you don't misrepresent your honey in any way.

It's a mistake to think that honey, while produced naturally by bees, meets the criteria for being labelled as 'organic', for example. In order to reach this status, the plants on which the bees feed must have been grown organically. Since bees are foraging in an radial area of about 5 km (3 miles), you can't guarantee that every farmer's field, every orchard and every garden that your bees visit is grown to certified organic standards.

To undertake honey production on a business scale not only requires necessary and enhanced skills, a suitable environment and all the equipment, but also relies on sound and accurate legal advice. Each country has its own rules and regulations regarding the production and sale of food products direct to the public. These rules cover hygiene, health and safety as well as the requisite labelling of produce. Furthermore, wherever you live it is most likely that the rules specific to honey mean that it must not be more than 19 per cent water by volume, and you may even be required to pasteurise it to meet food safety standards.

Before you start building a bee empire, why not test your skills and submit your honey to expert scrutiny, or consider entering a honey show. Your bee-keeping association will have the dates and venues of these, and whether you win a ribbon or not, you'll get a chance to meet and talk to your peers and get advice from experts.

Chapter 10   Pests and Diseases

A HEALTHY COLONY

As with all animals, bees are susceptible to a range of pests and diseases, but fortunately the beekeeper who pays close regard to hygiene and remains vigilant to the signs can do much to maintain a healthy, vigorous colony. Be aware: American foulbrood, European foulbrood, small hive beetle, acarine disease and varroa are among the bee diseases that are, in many countries, 'notifiable diseases', which means they must be reported to the appropriate inspectorate. Check with your country's national bee-keeping organisation for details.

Hygiene

Many diseases are introduced to a hive because bees visit other hives. It is also possible that beekeepers themselves introduce diseases. For that reason, you must routinely launder your bee-keeping suit and clean and disinfect boots, hive tools and equipment after each use at each hive to prevent cross-infections. This is especially important if you have a number of hives or, as a member of a club, you visit other hives.

Keep the area around a hive clear of debris. Remove dead bees from the ground and dispose of cappings and end-of-frame cells to reduce the chance of robbing and infestation. Previously used hive components – boxes, floors, crown boards, queen excluders – everything that the bees come into contact with, must be thoroughly scorched with a blowtorch before use. Plastic hives should be cleaned thoroughly with hypochlorite.

To reduce the chances of diseases ensure that:

- You keep up to date with new methods of pest and disease control.
- You maintain clear and accurate records to monitor your hive(s) and identify any medication administered.
- The apiary is kept clean and surrounding areas tidy.
- Your bees are sourced from a reputable supplier and are guaranteed disease-free.
- You avoid buying second-hand frames, as they can't be cleaned and sterilised effectively.

- You avoid interchanging hive parts between one hive and another.
- You combine weak colonies to form one strong colony.
- If your bees die, you close the hive to prevent other bees getting access to the honey and thereby spreading any disease further.

If the bees have to draw new combs from foundation each year for the brood nest or, better still, for the entire brood chamber, the risk of pathogens establishing themselves in the colony is greatly reduced.

It will take some time and experience to be able to tell if there's something wrong with your bees by assessing their behaviour, but the best way to watch their health is by routine inspection of the hive. The brood box should have frames with a consistent pattern of brood laying; pearly white larvae should have clearly visible body segments; uniform brood cappings should be light brown in colour; lively bees should be flying well with 'perfect wing'; and there should be stores of fresh-looking pollen and white-capped honey cells.

There should be no nasty odour in the hive, and it should always be free from damp and mould. If, in the course of your routine hive inspections, you are unhappy with what you see or are concerned that there may be a problem, contact your bee-keeping association or an experienced beekeeper, who will advise you.

DISEASES OF ADULT BEES

As soon as you suspect disease in your hives, immediately contact an expert via your bee-keeping association.

Acarine disease

This disease is caused by a mite *Acarapis woodi*, which penetrates a bee's trachea when it is between one and eight days old. The mite bites through the tracheal walls and feasts on the bee's blood (haemolymph). The puncture causes blood to block the bee's airways and when it cannot breathe, it cannot fly effectively, so can only hop around in front of the hive. Death from acarine disease usually occurs in bees in the winter, which leads to a spring dwindling of the colony. The expanding brood is left un-nursed and unattended and the colony is severely weakened. Seek advice and treatment via your association, and in countries where this disease is notifiable, contact the relevant inspectorate.

Varroa

The varroa mite (*Varroa jacobsoni*) is a mite that lives on both adult bees and on brood. The mites travel huge distances on the backs of bees and hives are infested as part of the natural process of swarming and robbing. If left untreated, the colony can die, but increasingly, the mite is becoming resistant to some of the treatments that have been effective in the past.

A varroa mite is about 1.5 mm (1/20th in) long and, because it is a reddish-brown colour, can easily be spotted on white larvae. The adult female mite enters a brood cell just before it is capped and will feed off the immature bee's haemolymph. She then also lays her own eggs in the cell, and the offspring mate there too. The mites escape when the bee emerges from the cell, but only the female mites will have survived to begin the cycle anew. The number of mites decreases in winter, when the queen bee takes a break from laying, but the remaining mites stay on the bees' backs as they huddle together in a ball, feeding off the adult bees' haemolymph.

Careful integrated pest management (IPM), using a mixture of chemical and non-chemical treatments, including the use of the important varroa screen floor (some 30 per cent of mites fall through the screen floor and are unable to return to the hive) and removing the drone brood (the mites seem very partial to these) is highly recommended. Placing a super frame in the brood box encourages worker bees to make hanging comb, which is usually drone brood. When the brood is capped, remove it from the hive, along with a great number of mites. Varroa strips impregnated with a thymol-based product can also be used.

A further method of IPM encourages the bees' own defensive actions by dousing them with fine icing sugar throughout the season. This may sound strange, but it encourages the bees to groom each other, thereby picking off any mites that are on their bodies. Your local bee-keeping association will have further details about IPM techniques and will run courses on IPM systems that are recommended by your national bee council.

Nosema

Nosema is a disease caused by a protozoan that affects a bee's digestive system: the bee effectively suffers from dysentery and the disease is spread in the hive as worker bees lick clean the mess to clear it away. Nosema is a debilitating disease, but is rarely fatal to a colony and can be treated with a proprietary medicine added to the sugar-solution feed. It's important to stress that the sugar-solution feeds themselves should not be made too dilute, as the excess water can cause bees to defecate prematurely in the hive. The solution should be made using granulated white sugar, as there is some evidence to suggest that brown and unrefined cane sugar can cause dysentery. Scrupulous hygiene is called for at all times. Cleaning all stored hive furniture and the fumigation of empty hives is a must.

BROOD DISEASES

Recognising brood diseases requires knowledge of what a healthy brood looks like. This is where practical knowledge and experience gained on training courses, working with experienced beekeepers and belonging to a local association pays dividends.

Foulbrood

Both foulbrood diseases – European foulbrood (EFB) and American foulbrood (AFB) – are notifiable diseases. Foulbrood is caused by bacterial infection. In AFB the infected bee larvae die in the cells, while with EFB, the unsealed brood is most affected. Because the two diseases present themselves in similar ways, beekeepers undertake a match test to distinguish between them. Here, a matchstick is inserted into a cell with dead larvae in it, twisted and pulled out again. The presence of the deadlier AFB is indicated when stringy filaments are drawn out by the match from the dead larvae. With EFB there are no filaments withdrawn.

EFB is caused by the bacterium *Streptococcus pluton*. Infection can be identified first by a sour odour in the hive and then by observing gaps in the brood nest

and discoloured, sunken and punctured cell cappings. In the early stages of the disease, inside the cells there are rubbery brownish-black-coloured smooth scabs. In some outbreaks where the colony is strong, the worker bees are able to deal with these and will remove them effectively from the hive. Later stage disease reveals the larvae to be dark brown in colour, dough-like to sticky or slimy in consistency and there are dead larvae in sealed and unsealed cells — usually lying in the lower part of the cell. Minor outbreaks of EFB can often be treated by shaking the colony into a new hive, but if this is ineffective, the hive and the colony must be destroyed.

AFB is caused by the bacterium *Bacillus larvae* and there is no known treatment, so the hive and colony must be destroyed. The indicators are the same as for EFB, but in this infection, the odour is more glue-like and bees are unable to remove the 'scabs' in the bottom of the cells.

Small hive beetle (SHB)

This is notifiable in many countries and originates in Africa, where the native species of bee deals effectively with it. Unfortunately, the European honeybee cannot cope with this tropical pest, unknowingly imported via container ports and airports. The beetle is dark brown, nearly black, oval in shape and about 7 mm (1/4 in) long and 4 mm (1/6th in) wide. It lives and breeds in the colony of honeybees. The female beetle lays thousands of eggs and the larvae then feed on the bees' brood, pollen and honey. The mass of larvae often congregate together, but when you open an infected hive, you will often see the beetles run for darkness in the corners while its white, three-legged larvae feed all over the brood. If you suspect an infection of SHB, contact your local bee-keeping association immediately.

Chalkbrood

More common but less serious is chalkbrood. Caused by a fungus that grows in a stressed colony, this can occur when there is a sharp drop in temperature after a warm spell in spring. The fungus grows and is ingested by the bee larvae, which then die, shrunken and hard. Their chalk-white remains can be seen on the hive's landing board as the worker bees attempt to remove the dead from the hive. A strong, vigorous colony can deal with chalkbrood, since their cluster is large enough to maintain the temperature of the brood with only the outer fringes becoming cool. But if the colony weakens and cannot keep warm, the brood may succumb to the disease. Cleaning out the brood frames and re-queening (see page 105) will help if the problem persists.

Sacbrood

This, fortunately, rare disorder is caused by a virus, the exact identity of which is unknown. And until its origins are established, there remains no treatment. The disease normally subsides on its own, but because of the manner in which it presents itself, it can be confused for one of the foulbrood diseases (a match test will present no filaments, however). Accompanying a strong sour smell in the hive are gaps in the brood and cell cappings are dark, sunken and punctured. Inside the cells there are yellowish-brown or dark-grey-coloured scabs (which the bees can remove). The larvae are grey-black, watery and granular in consistency. Dead larvae are to be found in capped and uncapped cells, usually with their heads sticking straight up.

Colony collapse disorder (CCD)

The headline-grabbing CCD has been dubbed a mystery plague and appears to have been most widespread among the commercial apiarists in North America, where bees have simply vanished from their hives. Causes are as yet unknown but research is ongoing, so it is vital that all beekeepers – hobbyists and professionals – remain vigilant and up to date with developments in bee journals and through local associations.

PESTS

In addition to mice, who enjoy nesting in hives in winter, a number of other nuisances present themselves, but all can be kept under control through correct hive management.

Bee louse

The bee louse *Braula coeca* is an insect with six legs and is about 1–1.5 mm in diameter. It usually attaches itself to the thorax of a bee and then steals food from its proboscis. A queen may have as many as 20 lice on her, although worker bees may have only one. The lice do no more harm than bother the bees, although affected queens may have reduced egg-laying activity. Using the IPM system (see page 137), a dusting of icing sugar encourages the bees to groom each other, or alternatively, a slip of paper sprinkled with naphthalene and placed under the combs in the hive in the evening and then removed the next morning is effective. The naphthalene paralyses the lice and they drop down onto the paper. Both paper and lice should be burned immediately.

Wax moth

Wax moths lay their eggs on both the combs in the hive and on combs that have been re-moved for storage. The emerging larvae make small indentations in the wood of the frames and inside the hive, before spinning a cocoon and pupating. They then move into the combs, where the moths start laying eggs among the brood. You need to be vigilant and keep an eye out for fine grey-coloured webs made by the larvae as they eat their way through the comb. In strong colonies, the bees keep the larvae in check by killing the emerging larvae and taking their bodies out of the hive. Any combs removed from the hive that you want to store in hive bodies or in storage cabinets should be fumigated two or three times after removal at three to four week intervals. Fumigants can be purchased from your bee supplier store. Store the combs at room temperature, or just below. A major wax moth infestation requires the nest to be burnt and the damaged combs cut out and melted down.

Wasps

Wasps normally only trouble sick bees, or bees unable to fly off the landing board in front of the hive. In spring you can use some wasp traps: plastic bottles with narrow necks, quarter filled with a thin honey and water solution or some sweet fruit juice. The scent attracts the wasps and they enter the bottle and drown. In autumn wasps may try to enter the hive, but usually the guard bees see them off. If many wasps attack at once, there is a danger they will rob the hive of its honey, so make sure the hive entrance is partially blocked in autumn to reduce the size of the entrance.

Ants

Ants can do quite a bit of damage, as they can chew through hives and invade the colony. Your bee supply store will be able to recommend a suitable ant bait to use in the hive. Ants are attracted to hives, especially when the sugar-solution feed is available, which is why extra care should be taken not to spill or dribble the solution on or around the hive.

Pesticides and herbicides

Pesticides and herbicides continue to present a great threat to the honeybee. Bees that come into contact with pesticides as they forage usually die – either instantly, or on their flight back to the hive. If a colony is foraging on a heavily sprayed crop, colony numbers can be severely diminished very quickly. Avoid using pesticides yourself and ask your neighbours to do the same. Fortunately, with increased knowledge about green issues, most gardeners are already following pesticide-free methods. Herbicides seldom kill honeybees, but they do unfortunately kill many of the plants that provide bees with their supplies of pollen and nectar. You, your neighbours, gardeners and fellow bee association members can all do much to lobby your local government to take steps to protect wild plants and weeds that grow at field edges, roadsides, on riverbanks and on lake shores. If it is essential that these plants are removed, lobby and campaign for mowing rather than spraying.

GLOSSARY

ACARICIDE A chemical preparation used to destroy mites.

ACARINE A disease caused by *Acarapis woodi* mites that affects a bee's breathing. It is also known as Isle of Wight disease, because of its first occurrence there in 1906.

AFRICANISED BEES Also known (erroneously) as 'killer bees', Africanised bees are a hybrid of the African honeybee (*Apis mellifera scutellata*) and several European honeybees. These bees do have a reputation for being more aggressive in the defence of their hives than their European cousins and have spread north and south from Brasil (where the first hybrids occurred).

AFTERSWARM The portion of a colony that leaves the parent hive with one or more virgin queens.

AMERICAN FOULBROOD (AFB) A notifiable disease in bees. The disease may occur anywhere in the world and is caused by a spore producing bacterium. There is no known treatment: infected hives, bee stock, honey and frames must be destroyed. See also European foulbrood (EFB).

ANTHER The part of a flower that releases pollen.

APIARY A collection of two or more hives with colonies of bees present.

BEE CAGE A device for safely introducing a new queen into the hive. The bee cage is a mesh cage that allows other bees to lick the queen for her queen substance and thus pass her pheromones around the hive without harming her. The cage is positioned between the frames of the brood chamber and the queen is kept inside by a plug of newspaper or sugar candy, which the beekeeper can remove after a few days or leave it in place to be chewed by the other bees.

BEEKEEPER'S BRUSH A very soft brush or large feather used to remove bees gently from a frame or to encourage them into a confined space.

BEE LANGUAGE The dancing or gestures by which information is communicated to the colony members, discovered and described by Professor Karl Ritter von Frisch (1886–1982), who received a Nobel Prize for his groundbreaking research.

BEE PASTURE Wild and cultivated plants, shrubs and trees that supply the bees with pollen, honeydew and nectar.

BEE SPACE A space of 7–8 mm (about 1/4 in) between the frames and the walls of a hive, needed for the bees to do their work. The space also allows the beekeeper to remove the frames to harvest honey. Spaces bigger than this are filled by the bees with propolis or honeycomb.

BEESWAX Worker bees excrete wax from eight glands located on the underside of the body between the abdominal segments. The bees use it to cap cells and build combs.

BEE YEAR The bee year begins in August, because bees hatched in this month are the ones that will rear the spring population.

BOTTOM BEE SPACE HIVE A hive in which frames hang in boxes with a space between the bottom of the frames and the box.

BRACE COMB A bridge of beeswax constructed between surfaces inside the hive.

BROOD The larval form of bees – from the egg to the capped off pupa.

BROOD BOX The part of the hive in which the queen is confined by a queen excluder and where the brood is reared.

BROOD CHAMBER The lower bee chamber where the young bees are raised.

CANDY A solid food made from sugar that is frequently used to separate queens in a new hive.

CAPPINGS The name given to a thin wax that covers the honey once it has been cut off the extracting frame. A source of premium beeswax.

CELL A single hexagonal compartment in a honeycomb.

CHALKBROOD A disease caused by a fungus Ascophaera apis, which causes the larvae to turn into chalky, white mummies.

CLEARER BOARD The board used to clear bees from the supers before harvesting the honey.

COLONY The group of worker bees, drones, queen and developing brood living together as a unit in a hive.

COMB The wax portion of the colony in which bees lay their eggs and store honey and pollen.

COMB HONEY Honey in the wax combs.

CROWN BOARD The board that is placed on the uppermost super and has a hole for ventilation.

DRONE A stingless male bee.

EUROPEAN FOULBROOD (EFB) An infectious brood disease caused by the bacterium *Streptococcus pluton*.

FANNING Rapid beating of the wings by bees near the entrance to the hive that causes air to move through, thus ventilating the hive.

FEEDER A device for feeding bees artificially.

FIELD BEE Another name for foragers – worker bees that are at least 21 days old and work outside the hive collecting pollen, nectar, water and propolis.

FLIGHT BOARD The wooden landing strip in front of a hive.

FLIGHT PATH Refers to the direction in which bees fly when leaving the colony. If the path is obstructed, the bees may become aggravated.

FOULBROOD A serious bee disease in the form of American foulbrood (AFB) and European foulbrood (EFB).

FOUNDATION A sheet of beeswax onto which a hexagonal pattern has been embossed that is the starting point for bees to build a comb. The foundation must be wax – bees will not build on any other material.

FRAME Four batons of wood forming a rectangle designed to hold the honeycomb.

GUARD A bee whose job it is to guard the hive and monitor who enters there.

HEFTING Lifting the hive with the roof on, but without supers, as a means of establishing weight. This allows the beekeeper to determine the weight of the colony and its food requirements.

HIVE SCENT All the worker bees in a colony produce a scent that is characteristic of their colony and that is recognised by all the bees in it.

HIVE TOOL A metal bar used for loosening combs.

HOFFMAN FRAME A self-spacing frame.

HONEY The sweet viscous material produced by bees. It is composed largely of a mixture of dextrose and levulose dissolved in about 19 per cent water. It contains small amounts of sucrose, minerals, vitamins, proteins and enzymes.

HONEY CHAMBER A chamber that is separated from the brood chamber by a queen excluder, with combs in which the honey is stored.

HONEY COLOUR Measured by a Pfund grader, honey colours are classified into 7 gradations from water white and white, to amber and dark amber.

HONEYDEW A sweet liquid excreted by some plant-feeding insects such as aphids and white flies.

HONEY FLOW The period when the greatest amount of nectar is available within the bee's flight range.

HONEY SAC The part of a bee's body where nectar is carried.

LANDING BOARD Also known as the alighting board, this is a strip of wood attached to the bottom of the hive that bees

land on before entering. It also allows the beekeeper to see what the bees are removing from the hive.

LANGSTROTH HIVE One of the most commonly used types of hives, named after it's inventor the Reverend L.L. Langstroth.

LAYING WORKERS These are worker bees that lay eggs in a queenless colony. Since the workers cannot mate, the eggs are infertile and produce drones.

LISTENING In winter, when the hive must not be opened, keepers listen to the bees humming inside by using a thin open tube with one end placed at the entrance to the hive and the other to their ear. The quality of the bees' humming is indicative of the condition of the colony.

MEAD Honey wine.

MOBBING A queen may be attacked by hostile bees that surround her in a tight ball or mob. She is usually killed or seriously injured.

MOUSE GUARD A grid that allows bees in and out of the hive but keeps mice out.

NASANOV GLAND A gland in a worker bee's abdomen that is used to attract bees back into the hive.

NATIONAL HIVE A square, single-walled hive that is most often used in the UK.

NECTAR The sweet, sugary substance produced by plants in order to attract pollinating insects and is made into honey by bees.

NOSEMA A disease caused by a protozoan *Nosema apis* that affects the guts of adult bees.

NUCLEUS Part of an established colony that is separated from the main colony and is without a queen and forms the beginning of a new colony.

NUPTIAL FLIGHT The mating flight made from the hive by a virgin queen to mate with drones.

NURSE BEE Any worker bee that is involved in rearing brood.

OPEN MESH FLOOR (OMF) This is increasingly being used to combat varroa.

PISTIL The female reproductive organ of a plant

POLLEN The dust-like grains that are produced by a plant's anthers and that are used to fertilise a female ovule.

POLLEN BASKET Also known as a pollen sac, the areas on the hind legs of a bee on which the pollen is transported to the hive. The basket – a hollow in the tibia – is surrounded by brush-like hairs, which allow the bee to scrape the pollen caught on its body hairs into the basket.

PORTER BEE ESCAPE A one-way exit for bees that's used in clearer boards.

PROPOLIS Used by the bees to block up holes and glue elements together inside the hive, propolis is collected by the bees from the bark and buds of trees.

QUEEN The sexually developed female bee who lays eggs.

QUEEN CELL A large cell on the face or bottom of a frame that houses a grub who is destined to become queen.

QUEEN EXCLUDER A grill through which the queen cannot pass and that separates the brood chamber from the first super thereby stopping egg laying in the honey storage area.

QUEEN MARKING GRID A device for holding the queen on the frame surface, allowing the beekeeper to mark her to display her age and make her more visible.

QUEEN SUBSTANCE A pheromone mixture that is licked off the queen by passing workers.

ROBBING When wasps and bees from other colonies steal honey from the hive.

ROYAL JELLY Sugar enriched brood food given to larvae in queen cells that helps them develop into queens rather than worker bees.

SAC BROOD A viral disease that causes the larvae to die before their final moult. Re-queening the hive is the usual solution.

SKEP An old-fashioned type of hive made of wicker or straw and without moveable frames. Generally used today only for catching swarms and not for rearing a colony. Illegal in some parts of the world.

SMOKER The device used by beekeepers to introduce cool smoke into a hive before it is opened. Suitable materials burned in the smoker include wood shavings, egg boxes, shredded newspaper, old hessian sacking, dried conifer and grass clippings.

STIGMA The part of a flower's pistil that receives the pollen during the pollination process.

STING The queen and worker bees – but not drones – have a barbed sting. When they use the sting, the barb keeps the sting in the wound but also leaves behind part of the bee's own viscera. This means that the bee dies.

STORES Honey stored around the brood chamber for feeding the larvae.

SUGAR SYRUP A solution of 50:50 sugar and water used to feed bees at times when no nectar is flowing or honey supplies are low.

SULPHUR CANDLE A device for killing off a colony if a disease makes this necessary.

SUPER The upper chamber(s) where the honey is stored.

SUPERSEDURE The bees' method of replacing their queen without swarming.

SWARMING When the bees try to split the colony in half and find a new home. Ideally a swarm would include a mated queen.

TANGING Making a loud noise, such as banging a spoon on a saucepan, in order to bring down a swarm that is flying overhead.

TOP BEE SPACE HIVE A hive in which the frames are suspended so there is a space above them and the top of the box.

VARROA A disease caused by a blood-sucking mite (*Varroa destructa*) that infests hives and debilitates bees.

VARROA STRIPS Plastic strips impregnated with insecticide that will kill the varroa mite in the hive.

WAGGLE DANCE The 'figure-of-eight' dance that bees use to communicate good places to forage.

WAX MOTHS Serious hive pests that damage stored comb. The larvae scoop out indentations in the wooden sides of the frames and hives where they pupate.

WBC HIVE Have designed by William Broughton Carr in 1890.

WINTER REST Bees survive the winter by clustering into a tight ball.

WORKER A sterile female bee.

WORKER COMB A comb measuring about two cells to the centimetre (five cells per inch) in which worker bees are reared and honey and pollen are stored.

Index

ACKNOWLEDGEMENTS

My thanks to Vic Swift at the British Library, London, and to Diana for constant support and endless cups of tea. Very special thanks go to Ed and Sara, Graeme, John and Louise, Martin, Josh, and to all the beekeepers in East Sussex, Kent and Surrey, who allowed me into their gardens, lent me a bee-keeping suit and let me learn from them as they tended their hives.

BIBLIOGRAPHY AND RESOURCES

Benjamin, Alison and McCallum, Brian, *Keeping Bees and Making Honey*, David & Charles (2008)
Butler, C.G., *The World of the Honeybee*, Collins (1974)
Dadant and Sons (eds), *The Hive and the Honeybee*, Dadant and Sons (1975)
Davies, Andrew, *Beekeeping*, Collins and Brown (2007)
Hartley, Dorothy, *Food in England*, Little, Brown (2006)
Hopper, Ted, *Guide to Bees and Honey*, Rodale Press (1977)
Hubbell, Sue, *A Book of Bees*, Mariner Books (1988)
Morse, Roger, *The Complete Guide to Beekeeping*, Dutton (1974)
Peacock, Paul, *Keeping Bees: A Complete Practical Guide*, Gaia Books (2008)
Root, A. I., *The ABC and XYZ of Bee Culture*, A.I. Root Co. (1978)
Snodgrass, R.E., *The Anatomy of the Honeybee*, Comstock (1956)

National Beekeeping Associations

American Beekeeping Federation
PO Box 1337, Jesup, Georgia, 31598-1038
www.abfnet.org

Australian Honey Bee Industry Council
www.honeybee.org.au

BBKA (British Beekeepers' Association)
National Agricultural Centre,
Stoneleigh,
Warwickshire, CV8 2LG
www.bbka.org.uk

Canada Honey Council
www.honeycouncil.ca

Canadian Association of Professional Apiculturalists
www.capabees.ca

The Federation of Irish Beekeepers Associations
www.irishbeekeeping.ie
International Bee Research Association
16 North Road,
Cardiff, CF10 3DY
www.ibra.org.uk

National Beekeepers Association of New Zealand
www.nba.org.nz

- HERGÉ -

LAS AVENTURAS DE TINTIN

STOCK DE COQUE

EDITORIAL JUVENTUD

**Las aventuras de TINTÍN Y MILÚ
están editadas en los idiomas siguientes:**

Afrikaans:	HUMAN & ROUSSEAU	Ciudad del Cabo
Alemán:	CARLSEN	Reinbek-Hamburgo
Árabe:	DAR AL-MAAREF	El Cairo
Asturiano:	JUVENTUD	Barcelona
Bengalí:	ANANDA	Calcuta
Bernés:	EMMENTALER DRUCK	Langnau
Brasileño:	DISTRIBUIDORA RECORD LTDA.	Río de Janeiro
Bretón:	AN HERE	Quimper
Castellano:	JUVENTUD	Barcelona
Catalán:	JUVENTUD	Barcelona
Coreano:	UNIVERSAL PUBLICATIONS	Seúl
Chino:	EPOCH PUBLICITY AGENCY	Taipeh
Danés:	CARLSEN/IF	Copenhague
Esperanto:	ESPERANTIX	París
	CASTERMAN	París-Tournai
Feroiano:	DROPIN	Thorshavn
Finlandés:	OTAVA	Helsinki
Francés:	CASTERMAN	París-Tournai
Galés:	GWASG & DREF WEN	Cardiff
Gallego:	JUVENTUD	Barcelona
Griego:	ANGLO HELLENIC	Atenas
Holandés:	CASTERMAN	Tournai-Dronten
Húngaro:	IDEGENFORGALMI PROPAGANDA ES KIADO VALLALAT	Budapest
Indonesio:	INDIRA	Yakarta
Inglés:	METHUEN & Co.	Londres
Inglés americano:	ATLANTIC. LITTLE BROWN	Boston
Islandés:	FJÖLVI	Reykiavik
Italiano:	COMIC ART	Roma
Japonés:	FUKUINKAN SHOTEN	Tokio
Latín:	ELI/CASTERMAN	Recanati/Tournai
Luxemburgués:	IMPRIMERIE ST. PAUL	Luxemburgo
Malayo:	SHARIKAT UNITED	Pulo Pinang
Noruego:	SEMIC	Oslo
Occitano:	CASTERMAN	París-Tournai
Persa:	UNIVERSAL EDITIONS	Teherán
Picardo turnaisense:	CASTERMAN	Tournai
Portugués:	VERBO	Lisboa
Romanche:	LIGIA ROMONTSCHA	Coira
Serbo-croata:	NIRO	Belgrado
Sueco:	CARLSEN/IF	Estocolmo
Vascuence:	ELKAR	San Sebastián

Vigesimoprimera edición, 2002

Artwork copyright © 1958 by Casterman, París-Tournai
© renewed 1986 by Casterman
© de la traducción española:
Editorial Juventud, 1962
Provença, 101 - 08029 Barcelona
www.editorialjuventud.es
editorialjuventud@retemail.es
Traducción del francés de Concepción Zendrera
Depósito legal: B.16.830-2002
ISBN 84-261-1003-7 (cartoné)
ISBN 84-261-1422-9 (rústica)
Número de edición de E. J.: 10.052
Impreso en España - Printed in Spain
Ediprint, c/. Llobregat, 36 - 08291 Ripollet (Barcelona)

STOCK DE COQUE

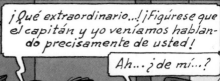

¡Qué extraordinario...! ¡Figúrese que el capitán y yo veníamos hablando precisamente de usted!

Ah... ¿de mí...?

Pues sí, señor, de usted... y entonces surge como el diablo de una caja sorpresa. Es algo inaudito. Pero... ¿qué es de su vida?

¿Yo...? Pues...bien... Sí, sí... Viajo... Pero...

...perdonen, tengo ahora mucha prisa. Voy a llegar tarde a una cita... Adiós.

¡Oh! ¡Qué lástima! En fin... De todos modos, tome mi dirección. Y a usted, mi general, ¿dónde se le puede localizar?

¡Ah! Pues...en el hotel... ¡ejem...!, en el hotel Brístol...

¡Ah! En el Brístol. ¿Y cuándo le po...?

Bueno... Y ahora me voy. ¡Adiós, amigos!

¡Hasta la vista, mi general!

Pues, francamente, no parecía muy contento de hablar con nosotros tu general Alcázar.

¡Qué hombre tan raro! Vamos, pasemos ahora...

? ¡OH!

¡Canastos! La cartera del general. Al guardarla le habría resbalado del bolsillo.

Corra, no puede estar muy lejos.

¡Anda! ¿Dónde se habrá metido?

Quizá haya tomado un coche... Es igual, el hotel Brístol está a dos pasos. Depositaremos allí la cartera.

Unos instantes más tarde, en el Brístol...

¿El general Alcázar...? No, señor, no hay nadie aquí de ese nombre...

Quizás esté inscrito con otro nombre...
¿Ramón Zárate...?

Ramón Zárate... no, señor... ¿Es español?

Un sudamericano bastante corpulento, de barbilla prominente, con bigotito... Aguarde, se lo dibujaré...

Es más o menos así...

No, señor, lo siento, pero no conozco a esta persona

Pues es raro... Bueno, muchas gracias.

¿Qué hacemos ahora para devolverle la cartera a ese fenómeno?

Eso estoy pensando.

Pero... quizá la cartera nos dé la solución para localizar al general.
Venga, entremos en ese café...

Denos... e... e... e... Veamos... veamos...

Dos vasos de agua mineral.

Y ahora examinemos lo que contiene.

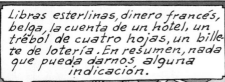

Libras esterlinas, dinero francés, belga, la cuenta de un hotel, un trébol de cuatro hojas, un billete de lotería. En resumen, nada que pueda darnos alguna indicación.

... Y en este sobre, fotos de aviones... ¡Qué curioso!, ¿verdad, capitán?

¡Ah! Una carta. Ahora sí que creo que tenemos una pista.
¡Vea, capitán!

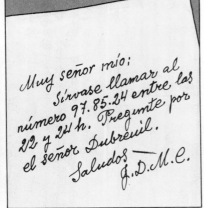

Muy señor mío:
Sírvase llamar al número 97.85.24 entre las 21 y 24 h. Pregunte por el señor Dubreuil.
Saludos.
J.D.M.C.

Pero ahí no está la dirección del general...

Ya lo sé, pero llamaremos al número de teléfono que dice esta carta.

¿Oiga, es el 97.85.24? ¿Podría hablar con el señor Dubreuil? ¿Quién soy...? Un amigo del general Alcázar, y yo... ¿OIGA...?

③

¿Cómo...? ¡El nombre de Alcázar no le dice nada...? ¿Y el de Ramón Zárate...? Entonces, señor... Es que he encontrado su cartera y quisiera... ¡Dispense!

Le repito, caballero, que no soy el señor Dubreuil, que no conozco a su general Alhambra y que todas estas historias no tienen nada que ver conmigo. ¡Conque... aire!

¡Qué individuo más grosero...!

Es raro... En ese número no lo conocen... Nada, dejémoslo. Ya hemos hecho todo lo posible. Volvámonos a Moulinsart.

Un poco después...

¡La puerta está abierta!

¡GUAUUU...! ¡GUAUUU...!

¿Qué te pasa, pobrecito Milú? ¿Quién te ha disfrazado de este modo?

Pero... ¿qué es lo que ha pasado aquí?

¿Qué le ha ocurrido, capitán?

¡Mil millones de demonios! ¡Quién es el pedazo de calabacín que me ha gastado esta broma...? ¡Néstor...! ¡Néstor...!

¡AAAAAH!

¡A...a...ahí, detrás de ti!

¡GRRRR!

4

¡ABDALLAH...!
¡GROUGGH!

¡ABDALLAH...?

¡ABDALLAH...!

¡Abdallah...! ¡Mil rayos...!

¡Hazlo otra vez, Mil Rayos...! ¡Vuelve a caerte por la escalera!

¿Qué es lo que estás haciendo aquí..., mala semilla?

Espera, espera, Mil Rayos; tráigo algo para ti.

¿Algo para mí...?

Sí, un regalo.

¡Un regalo...! Que sin duda ha traído de su país especialmente para mí. Pobrecillo. Tiene buen corazón el chico.

Toma, Mil Rayos, esto es para ti.

¡Gracias, Abdallah!

¡Un cucú...! ¡Es magnífico...! ¡Es precioso, Abdallah!

Ves, para darle cuerda...

...se hace así.

¡Mil millones de rayos y truenos! ¡Si esto crees que va a terminar aquí...!

¡GÜEE! ¡GÜEE!

¡Alto...! ¡Tú no tocar hijo de mi Emir

? ?

Yo, Hassim, servidor de Su Alteza Abdallah...

...y yo traer carta de mi Emir.

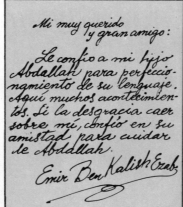

Mi muy querido y gran amigo:

Le confío a mi hijo Abdallah para perfeccionamiento de su lenguaje. Aquí muchos acontecimientos. Si la desgracia caer sobre mí, confío en su amistad para cuidar de Abdallah.

Emir Ben Kalish Ezab

Eso es para ti, Tintín... Y tú, Hassim, cuéntame los acontecimientos de que me habla el Emir.

Yo no saber, señor.

¿Qué te parece a ti todo esto? Lo único que está claro es que nos ha caído la lotería con el niño Abdallah. Será cuestión de domarlo.

¡Abdallah... mala peste, voy a darte una paliza...!

¡GÜEE...!

¡Alto, tú no tocar al hijo de mi Emir!

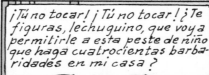

¡Tú no tocar! ¡Tú no tocar! ¿Te figuras, lechuguino, que voy a permitirle a esta peste de niño que haga cuatrocientas barbaridades en mi casa?

¡Espera un poco que te encuentre, ganapán!

Señor... señor... Es espantoso... Todos estos extranjeros se han instalado...

Espera, Néstor, espera un momento...

...en medio del salón.

A la mañana siguiente...

RRRING RRRING ?

¿DIGA?

¡Mil millones de mil rayos y truenos!

Ya va... Ya va... Ya voy.

RRRING RRRING

RRRING

¡Diga..., diga...! ¿Qué? ¿Cómo...? ¿Por quién pregunta...? ¡No, señora, no es aquí la carnicería Sanzot!

✦!!!+☉♗★❋ ⚡❋!>>❮❀⚛!

BLUB BLUB BLUB BLUB PLACH

RRRING

¡!?

Oye, deben de estar todos durmiendo aún...

Yo diría más: creo que están...

¡DIGA!

¡Diga...! ¿Quién...? ¿Hernández...? Ah, sí, con F... Diga, diga...

Yo... ¿Le molesto ahora quizá?

No, no, en absoluto. Diga,.. diga.

¿Si Tintín estará aquí esta mañana...? Sí... ¿Para hablarle? Bueno. ¿Cómo? ¿Qué dice? ¿Si conocemos al general Alcázar...? Sí, ¿por qué?

Luego se lo explicarán. Bueno, bueno... ¿Cómo...? No, no me han molestado nada.

¡Acaso les llamo yo a ellos por teléfono cuando se bañan?

Conque Hernández y Fernández quieren hablarme del general Alcázar... ¡Qué cosa más rara!, ¿verdad?

Sí. A propósito de cosas raras, esta mañana todavía no hemos visto a Abdallah.

KHRRR KHRRR

¡Mil truenos, ahí está!

No, ¡es el profesor Tornasol!

¡Dios mío!

¿Le da a menudo la locura de venir a desayunarse con los patines puestos?

Muy bien, gracias, ¿y usted?

Pero confesará que le intriga verme llegar de este modo... Sí, sí, le parece algo raro, no lo niegue...Bien, pues no puedo explicarle nada por el momento...

RRRRING

...pero dentro de poco comprenderá mis razones.

¿Los Fernández ya?

¿Cree usted?

¡Ah! Y ahora, a desayunar.

RIIIIING
BANG.

¡Qué fenómeno de hombre! ¡Rayos y truenos! ¿Ha terminado de hacer bobadas?

¿Quién llamaba, Néstor?

La primera vez no vi a nadie, señor, pero la segunda vi a Abdallah que se escapaba.

RIIIING

¡Será él, seguro! No quedará aquí la cosa, verás lo que le hago. Néstor, tráigame la manguera...

Bueno, en cuanto llame, tú abres la puerta y entonces yo: pschtt... Verás qué risa...

RIIIING

Ahí está. ¡Abre la puerta, Néstor!

Lo siento de veras. Perdonen. Tuvo la culpa Abdallah, ¿comprenden? Ese arrapiezo llamaba a la puerta y... ejem...

¡Ja, ja, ja, ja!

?

Unos instantes después...

Ejem... Se trata de lo siguiente: la Interpol nos ha encargado vigilar a un sujeto inglés, actualmente en el Continente, y recoger la máxima información acerca de sus actividades.

... y acerca de las personas con las que él se relaciona. Usted conoce a una de ellas: el general Alcázar. ¿Qué sabe usted de él?

¡Oh! A decir verdad, poca cosa...

Le conocí cuando era presidente de la república de San Theodoros (1). Luego le vi en Europa. Derrotado por su rival el general Tapioca, había huido de su país y se convirtió en lanzador de puñales en un teatro de variedades...(2) y... nada más.

¿De verdad nada más? ¿Qué le dijo ayer cuando usted lo encontró?

?

(1) Ver "LA OREJA ROTA"
(2) Ver "LAS 7 BOLAS DE CRISTAL"

Panel 1:
¡Ah, ah...! ¿Conque le extraña, jeh? Olvida usted, querido amigo, que nuestro oficio es saberlo todo.

Yo diría más: que nuestro todo es saberlo oficio.

Panel 2:
Sí, es verdad, le encontramos ayer noche; iba a decírselo. Pero...¿Qué nos dijo? Que viajaba, que tenía prisa y que paraba en el hotel... ee... ee... en el hotel...

Excelsior, sí, ya lo sabemos.

Panel 3:
Eso será, no nos contó nada más. Pero, díganme ¿qué se le reprocha?

¡Abrocha! ¡Ah! Perdón. Reprocha. Querido, si cuenta con que nosotros le revelemos que se trata de tráfico de aviones, se equivoca. En boca cerrada no entran moscas, ésa es nuestra divisa.

Panel 4:
¡Bien dicho! Yo aún diría más. En mosca cerrada no entran bocas. Que ese general haya venido a Europa para negociar la compra de aviones usados, no seremos nosotros los que se lo digamos a usted. Hasta la vista...

¡Hasta la vista!

Panel 5:
¡Ah! Nos traen los bastones y los sombreros.

Panel 6:
¡Qué raro, mi sombrero ha encogido!

¡Qué curioso, a mí me pasa al revés! Parece que se me ha hinchado la cabeza.

Panel 7:
¡Ah!, ya lo entiendo, es que nos hemos equivocado: tú te has puesto mi sombrero y yo el tuyo.

Eso es, tú te has puesto tu sombrero y yo el mío; bueno..., al revés.

Panel 8:
Pero si es lo mismo...

Yo también...

Panel 9:
¿A ver? Temo que Abdallah tenga algo que ver con esto.

¿Abdallalah...?

Panel 10:
Sí, me lo figuraba...es la clásica bromita de meter trozos de periódicos doblados bajo la badana del sombrero.

Panel 11:
Y un poco después...

¡Qué demonio ese Abdallah!

Panel 12:
¿Qué querían los hermanos siameses?

(1) Ver "EL LOTO AZUL"

Un cuarto de hora después...

Ya estamos en las afueras. ¡Ah! Parece que frena y va a girar...

Es aquí, chófer, pare.

¡Lástima, un guardián!

¿Cómo entrar sin que me vea...? Quizás... Sí, probaré.

Bueno, ya hemos cruzado el primer obstáculo. Veamos ahora.

¡Aviones, eso es!

¡Cuidado, se oyen pasos!

Buenos días, patrón. ¿Ha visto el diario de esta mañana? ¿No? Pues lea esto.

¡Ah, bravo! ¡Los "Mosquitos" que les servimos han hecho un buen trabajo! Los muchachos ya saben el modo de utilizarlos.

Ya lo creo. Y de lo de Alcázar, ¿qué hay?

El asunto está en el saco. Doce "Mosquitos" también, para ayudarle a derrotar a su rival el general Tapioca. Allá se las compongan ellos. ¡A nosotros qué! Mientras les endosemos nuestros saldos...

¡Claro, eso es! Bueno, voy a vigilar el empaquetado de las piezas de recambio para el DC3 del Arabair. Ahora que éste tiene el campo libre allá, los va a necesitar. Y apuesto a...

RRRR RRRR

¿Qué es esto...? ¿Qué pasa...? ¿Qué trasto es esté...?

¿De dónde viene ese timbre?

¡Un despertador!

¡Este Abdallah es más malo que la peste! Seguro que ha sido él quien me puso el despertador en el bolsillo.

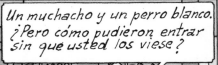

Un muchacho y un perro blanco. ¿Pero cómo pudieron entrar sin que usted los viese?

¿"Las Noticias"? Tome

Gracias.

¡CANASTOS!

¡Dios mío! ¿Qué pensará el capitán acerca de esto?

Y un poco después...

¡Abdallah, ya verás cuando te pille...!

¡Ja, ja! ¡Ja, ja!

Pobre crío. Es demasiado pequeño para enterarse de la gravedad de la situación.

BANG
?!

¡Mil millones de millones de naufragios! ¡Ya está bien! No puedo más, ese granuja, ese cólera... Un petardo bajo mi butaca mientras hacía la siesta... Se acabó; se lo devuelvo a su padre.

Ya no es posible, lea...

GOLPE DE ESTADO EN EL KHEMED

WADESDAH EN MANOS DE LAS FUERZAS REBELDES

LOS REVOLUCIONARIOS DEBEN LA VICTORIA A SU AVIACIÓN

PERO DE DÓNDE PROVIENEN ESOS «MOSQUITOS», ES UN MISTERIO...

El Sheik El Ehr, que ha tomado el poder.

(De nuestro corresponsal) Beirut, 15 Las fuerzas aéreas han jugado un definitivo ...ado las princi-

El emir Ben Kalish Ezab, prisionero de los rebeldes

EL CONSEJO ...URIDAD

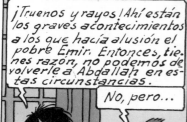
¡Truenos y rayos! Ahí están los graves acontecimientos a los que hacía alusión el pobre Emir. Entonces, tienes razón, no podemos devolverle a Abdallah en estas circunstancias.

No, pero...

...quizá haya otra solución. Si él no puede irse, nadie impide que nos marchemos nosotros.

Tintín, eso es una buena idea, pero ¿adónde iremos?

¿Dónde...? Pues al Khemed.

Eso es, muy bien, al Khemed.

¿Cómo dices? ¿Al Khemed? ¿En plena revolución? Tú estás loco. ¿Qué iríamos a buscar allá abajo?

Quizás podríamos liberar al Emir e intentar aclarar un asunto que me parece algo turbio.

No, niño, no cuentes conmigo... Vete tú, yo me quedo aquí.

PAM

Bueno, te acompañaré...

¿Un chico con un perro blanco? Me recuerda algo, pero ¿qué...?

RRRING
RRRING

Diga. ¿Quién es? ¡Ah!, ¿es usted, general Alcázar? ¿Su cartera...? ¿que la recuperó?

Sí, me la han devuelto. Un tal capitán Haddock, que encontré ayer, en compañía de un amigo mío, Tintín... ¿Cómo...? Sí, Tintín ¿le conoce usted? ¿Qué?, ¿La llamada de ayer? Sí, era él, había encontrado su número de teléfono en mi cartera.

¡Conque Tintín otra vez metiendo las narices en mis asuntos! ¡Ah, pues tomaré mis medidas para evitarlo!

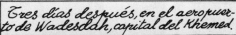

Tres días después, en el aeropuerto de Wadesdah, capital del Khemed.

Ahora llega el avión de Beirut.

¿Lo has entendido bien? Si él va dentro, pones esta maleta donde los equipajes.

WADESDAH
AEROPUERTO

Me alegro de haber llegado... Con esos pajarracos viejos, uno no sabe nunca...

¿Se ha fijado usted? Hay soldaditos armados por todos los rincones.

Pasaportes, "please", "gentlemen".

Lo siento, "gentlemen", no están autorizados para quedarse en el Khemed. Deben regresar, con el mismo avión, a Beirut.

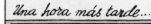

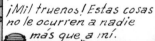

¡Como Milú que me llamo, me huelo que ahí dentro se esconde algo diabólico! Tengo que advertir en seguida a Tintín.

Estoy pensando QUIÉN ha podido anunciar nuestra llegada a las autoridades de Wadesdah y QUIÉN ha logrado que no nos admitieran.

Ven aquí, Milú. ¿Qué te pasa?

¡GUAU! ¡GUAU!

¿Quieres dejarme de una vez? ¡Qué pesado! Pero parece que desea enseñarme algo. Voy, te sigo...

¡GUAU! ¡GUAU!

¿Ahí dentro? Están los equipajes... ¿Quieres que entre? Bueno, ya voy...

¡GUAU! ¡GUAU!

TI-I-I-I-IT

?

TI-I-I-I-IT

¿Qué es ese ruido de sirena...?

الخذر يبقه

Fuego en un motor. Lo que se oía era el ruido del extintor.

Pero ¡truenos! Ese trasto no funciona y arde cada vez más.

¿Oiga, oiga? Aquí KH-OZD... A la torre de control de Wadesdah... Motor derecho ardiendo... Extintores inoperantes... Intentaremos llegar a Wadesdah...

No puedo. ¡Suerte de hombre la mía! Pesa demasiado, sin embargo, tengo que...

TAC TIC TAC TIC TAC

¿Oiga? Aquí KH-OZD... Motor derecho sigue ardiendo... Motor izquierdo ratea. Perdemos altura...

¡Ah! Ahora sí que es necesario que ese cabeza de chorlito venga a examinar este trasto.

¿Otra vez? No, amigo, ya está bien... No es éste momento para jugar.

¡Un paracaídas, exijo que me den un paracaídas!

¿Vienes a ver eso, sí o no?

Calma, señor... Un paracaídas, ahora, no le serviría de nada, y...

Le digo que quiero un paracaídas; he pagado mi billete, y yo...

Oiga, joven, un poquito de serenidad, ¡qué caramba!, y deje al piloto tranquilo ahora; tiene otros cabos que atar...

Mil perdones, pero...

O.K., muchacho, y gracias. Ahora que todo el mundo se sujete bien; probaré de aterrizar.

¿Oiga, oiga? Aquí KH-OZD... Sobrevolamos la costa sur de Kadeïh... Hemos vaciado los depósitos... Paramos el motor de la izquierda... Voy a intentar el aterrizaje...

¡Alá es grande! Estamos salvados.

¡Uf!, el fuego ya está apagado.

Pero no nos quedemos aquí a pleno sol, vamos a la sombra de estas rocas mientras esperamos los socorros.

¡Sal de ahí, Milú! ¡En seguida!

¡Guau, guau!

¡Guau, guau!

No hay que preocuparse, en Wadesdah están ya enterados. Dista cincuenta kilómetros de aquí. No tardarán en venir a buscarnos.

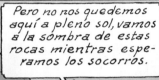

Unos instantes después...

Oiga, capitán, si nos quedamos aquí, nos van a llevar a Wadesdah y nuevamente nos expulsarán de allí... ¡Un instante, Milú! Según dicen, la ciudad está sólo a cincuenta kilómetros. ¿Qué le parece si nos marchamos a la francesa?

¿A pie?

¡Guau, guau!

A pie, claro. Pero ahora vuelvo al avión; este cabezota de Milú está empeñado en enseñarme algo...

¡Guau! ¿Te decides de una vez?

Ya voy, Milú, ya voy...

¡Cincuenta kilómetros! ¡Casi nada!

Cincuenta kilómetros... y sólo me queda... veamos... sólo me queda...

...medio litro de "whisky.". Eso significa un litro cada cien kilómetros... No es mucho, pero... ¡en fin!

WHAM

¡Mi botella...! ¡Que no se rompa mi botella!

¡Truenos, el aparato ha hecho explosión!

¡Pero la botella está intacta!

¡Dios mío! ¿Y Tintín?

Se había ido hacia el avión. Con tal que... ¡Cuidado! No rompamos mi botella.

¡TINTIN...! ¡TINTIN...!

ÓZING

¡Mil millones de mil naufragios!

¡Muchacho! ¿Nada roto...? ¿No estás herido?

No, no... Me caí al suelo debido a la onda explosiva. ¿Y Milú...? ¿Dónde está Milú?

Sano y salvo, y trae tu sombrero.

Milú, mi querido Milú, tú habías olido el peligro, y yo que creía que querías jugar...

Sí, Tintín, sí, muchas veces te equivocas al no tomarme más en serio.

Una bomba de relojería en el departamento de los equipajes; gracias al incendio del motor derecho estamos todavía con vida... Normalmente, a esta hora hubiésemos estado volando sobre Djebel... ¿Te das cuenta, si la explosión se hubiese producido en pleno vuelo?

Sí, nos hemos salvado de milagro, y me pregunto si...

¿Qué...?

No, nada; pero créeme, capitán, no echemos raíces aquí. Aire.

Pues como tú quieras.

En cuanto lleguemos a Wadesdah, pediremos hospitalidad al señor Oliveira de Figueira (1)

SNIFF SNIFF

Hemos de evitar encontrarnos con la expedición de socorro..., pues en cuanto reparen en nuestra huida, van a buscarnos.

GUAUUU
¡AYYY...! ¡AYYY...!

Llegó la noche...

Ya estoy harto de tu excursioncita; si esto dura mucho se me gastarán los pies hasta las rodillas. ¡Si pudiera echarme...

¡Echarse? Tenemos que llegar a Wadesdah antes de que amanezca; por lo tanto no hay posibilidad de echarse...

¡Échese, corra!

¿En qué quedamos, me echo o no me echo?

¡Una patrulla! Estoy seguro que nos buscan.

¡Alto! ¿Quién va?

He oído un ruido como de un ronquido.

¡Ah, sí! Es un avión, escucha...

¡Se lo suplico, deje de roncar!

¿Yo, roncar...? No he oído nada.

Uf... ya han pasado.

¡Ah, bueno...! RRR...

Vamos, capitán, arriba. Hemos de seguir...

Néstor: el desayuno en la cama... RRR...RRR...

No soy Néstor, capitán, soy Tintín... Levántese, de prisa...

RRR

¿Qué hacer, Dios mío? Mientras no vuelvan por aquí...

RRR... RRR...RRR...

(1) Ver "LOS CIGARROS DEL FARAON" y "TINTIN EN EL PAIS DEL ORO NEGRO".

Vamos, éste es el momento de utilizar la botellita de ron que reservo para los casos de urgencia.

¡Caramba con el tapón, no quiere salir...!

¡Ah, ya sale...! CLUC

CLUC = ▯ ☼☼☼ = 🍾 ☼☼☼ = WHISKY

¡Aaaah...! Y ahora, ¿dónde están los tipos esos de la patrulla? Voy a decirles c... c... cuatro cosas...

¡Chist...! ¡Silencio...! Hemos de seguir...

Y tarde, por la noche...

¡Por fin Wadesdah! Y ahora, prudencia... Las salidas importantes deben estar guardadas, pero conozco una puertecita que seguramente no lo estará.

¡Alto, todo no...!

¿Ve usted? Hemos pasado sin dificultad. Ahora tenemos que encontrar la casa del señor Oliveira de Figueira. Creo que está por aquí...

Ahí es, ya me acuerdo.

¿Y dices que siempre tiene un vinillo rosado fresquito?

¡Señor Oliveira...! ¡Señor Oliveira...!

¡Sería el colmo que se hubiese mudado!

¡Señor Oliveira...! ¡Señor Oliveira...! Soy Tintín, abra...

?

¡Mil naufragios! ¡Una patrulla!

Corra, escondámonos donde sea...

¿Quién es?

Aquí patrulla... ¿Qué hay?

¿Cómo qué hay? Soy yo quien pregunta, ¿no? ¡No se despierta a la gente a estas horas!

Oiga, no es culpa nuestra si usted tiene el sueño tan ligero...

¡Sueño ligero! ¡Qué frescura, después del ruido que han hecho...!

Bueno, pues la próxima vez andaremos con las manos para no despertar al noble señor Oliveira...

¡Que se os lleve el diablo!

Escuchad eso... A éste por lo menos no le impedimos dormir. ¡Qué música! ¡Ja, ja, ja, ja, ja!

¡Ji, ji, ji, ji! ¡Jo, jo, jo!

RRR RRR

¡Uf, ya han pasado...! ¡Qué susto! ¡Vamos, capitán, deje de roncar, por lo que más quiera!

SE BUSCA
TINTÍN
HADDOCK

RRR RRR RRR

¡Otra vez?

TOC TOC TOC

¡Por la barba de vuestro profeta! ¿Me dejaréis dormir, sí o no?

¡Abra, señor Oliveira! ¡Soy Tintín... ¡Abra, por favor!

Tintín. ¿Tú aquí...? ¡Entra, corre, por el amor de Dios!

RRR RRR RRR

¿Qué haces aquí, desgraciado? ¿No sabes que han puesto precio a tu cabeza?

Lo sé, acabo de leerlo en un cartel.

Buenas noches a todos.

¡Es increíble, inaudito, no lo concibo...! Pero, oye, ahora que lo pienso, debes de tener hambre.

¡Ya lo creo!

RRR RRR

...¿Y sed?

Ejem... dicen que tiene usted un vinillo rosado muy refrescante...

Ahora explíquenme por qué se encuentran en el Khemed.

Pues verá...

Fue Abdallah que nos...

...aviones en venta...

...una carta del Emir...

...tomamos el avión para Wadesdah...

Entonces decidimos seguir a pie para Wadesdah y venir a su casa.

Hicisteis bien. Ahora yo os pondré al corriente de la situación en el Kemed. Hace seis meses...

RRR RRR RRR

¡A LAS ARMAS!

?!

Yo...¿Qué pasa? Ejem...perdonen, creo que estaba soñando...una pesadilla. Unos...unos piratas que...

¡Ah, bueno!

Voy a fumarme una pipa. Me ayudará a seguir despierto.

¡Excelente idea!

¿Qué le estaba yo diciendo? ¡Ah, sí! Que hace seis meses, de resultas de un acuerdo entre el Emir y el Arabair, Wadesdah se convirtió en una escala importante de las líneas aéreas de la Meca. Pero últimamente ha habido, según parece, un conflicto entre el Arabair y el Emir y las cosas han empezado a estropearse.

Como si fuese por casualidad, han surgido conflictos por todo el país y el Sheik Bab El Ehr (1) se ha puesto a la cabeza de los rebeldes. Éstos, apoyados por una potente aviación, que, por cierto, parece que les ha caído del cielo, han ocupado Wadesdah y han tomado el poder.

Lo que es inquietante, señor Oliveira, es que los "Mosquitos" de los rebeldes y los DC 3 del Arabair tienen la misma procedencia...¿Y se sabe por qué ha estallado el conflicto entre el Emir y el Arabair?

Pues...no, ni la menor idea.

¡Ah, bueno! Ya veremos eso después. Ahora lo primero es ayudar al Emir. ¿Qué ha sido de él?

Ha debido de huir y refugiarse en el Djebel, en la guarida de Patrash Pacha (2) y sus feroces guerrilleros que le son fieles.

¡AAYYYYYY!

¡Ay! ¿Qué...qué... me ha pasado...?

Su pipa, le ha quemado la barba, capitán.

Vamos, es hora de ir a dormir. Mañana hallaremos el medio de hacerles salir de la ciudad y reunirnos con el Emir

Bien, de acuerdo.

Al cabo de dos días, por la mañana

¿Has visto? Viene una patrulla.

Ya sé, tranquilícese...

MIL TRUE...

(1) Ver "TINTIN EN EL PAIS DEL ORO NEGRO"
(2) Ver "LOS CIGARROS DEL FARAON"

¡Ja, ja, ja, ja, ja!   ¡Ji, ji, ji, ji, ji!
¡Jo, jo, jo, jo, jo!

¡OOOOH!
¡Oh, qué bueno!

¿Qué me dices de esto?

¡Guau, guau!
¿Quieres callarte, Milú?

Capitán, por poco nos la cargamos.
Sí, suerte que tuvimos todo el día de ayer para entrenarnos... ¡Pobre señor Oliveira!

¿Cántaros? Lo siento, señora, no me queda ni uno. Los estoy esperando...

Bueno, ya estamos fuera de la ciudad.
Y aquí está la fuente... ¡Vaya, nos había dicho que a esta hora no habría nadie!

صباح آلخير دمسّحڪ آلخير يا ڪﻻآڬ

لا تعڬن ترحوالى

آننا ننايبف ڬفڬحمك ﻫ بيبني وحڪ

¿Podría hablar español como todo el mundo, especie de Fátima de baratillo? ¿Qué es lo que quiere usted de mí?

¡GUAU!

¡Mil millones de millares de naufragios, esta loca va a dar la voz de alarma!

...Y nuestro guía no está aquí. Oliveira nos había dicho que estaría cerca de la fuente con los caba-llos... ¿Qué ocurre, Milú?

¡Guau! ¡Guau!

¡Aquí está! Estupendo, estoy deseando volver a montar.

Unos instantes después...

¡Mis estribos, mil naufragios, mis estribos...!

Mientras tanto...

¿Oiga, el coronel Ahmed? Aquí Mull Pachá, del Cuartel General de Sheik Bab El Ehr... Orden a tus "Mosquitos" de despegar inme-diatamente... ¿Diga...? Sí, misión de aniquilar grupo de tres hombres que han salido de Wadesdah en dirección a Djebel... ¿Diga? ¿Comprendido...? Bien... Les siguen jeeps blindados... ¿Diga? Sí, son partidarios de Ben Kalish Ezab... Sí, aniquilarlos.

¡Aquí están! ¡Fuego...!

¡Oigan, en el desierto hay un ataque aéreo!

BOM BOM
PAK PAK-PAK-PAK
PAK-PAK

Nuestros propios aviones... ¿Se han vuelto locos?

¡Oiga! Aquí "Pantera Negra". Primera misión cumplida; los dos jeeps blindados están en llamas.

¡Diga! ¿Sí? ¿Misión cumplida? ¡Perfecto! ¿Los dos jeeps blindados destruidos? Les felicito, coronel Amed, tus pilotos son unos ases...

¿Los jeeps blin... QUÉ?

¡Rápido, póngame otra vez con el coronel Ahmed! ¡Ah!, eres tú... Seguramente he comprendido mal! Tú no me has dicho que los jeeps blindados

... habían sido destruidos... Pues claro que sí, tal como tú ordenaste; ya he felicitado a los pilotos de tu parte... ¿Qué dices?

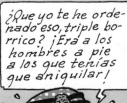
¿Que yo te he ordenado eso, triple borrico? ¡Era a los hombres a pie a los que tenías que aniquilar!

... Consejo de guerra... Juicio... Condena... Degradación...

Mientras tanto...
No me extrañaría que nos estuvieran buscando...

Bueno, ya han pasado. Montemos, todavía queda mucho camino.

A la mañana siguiente de madrugada...

RRR-RRR

¡Cuidado! ¡Cada uno al suyo!

27

RRRR

¡ALTO!

¡Amigos! ¡Amigos! ¡No tiréis!

¿Amigos? Vamos a ver, la consigna...

Los camellos ladran. ¡Ay, no! Los perros ladran, la caravana pasa.

Bueno, adelante. ¿Quién son estos extranjeros?

Amigos de Ben Kalish Ezab que han hecho un largo viaje para verle.

Bien; les llevaremos a su presencia.

¿Estos agujeros en las rocas? Sí, ya lo he notado, parecen ventanas... Se diría que vive gente ahí dentro.

Anda, anda, eso no es posible. Voy a cerciorarme de todos modos.

¿Eso habitado? ¡Qué tontería!

لحت شي ذزبد اكي شنوّيّت دا؟

¡Oh, perdone, señora...!

¡Tienes razón, Tintín, está habitado!

Yo... ¡Oh, mire usted!

¡Truenos, un templo romano tallado en la roca! Es formidable.

Ya hemos llegado.

Unos instantes después...

Prodigioso, es una verdadera ciudad excavada en la roca.

¡Tintín! ¡Capitán! ¡Ustedes aquí...! ¡Me parece imposible!

¿Y mi hijo? ¿Mi queridísimo pajarito de las islas? ¿Dónde está mi tesoro?

Le hemos dejado en Europa, Alteza... pero no se preocupe, está en buenas manos.

¡Pobre corderito! ¡Qué desgraciado debe de ser tan lejos, de su papá!

Y ahora te dejaré atado a tu palmera para que vengan los cocodrilos a devorarte... ¡Ja, ja! ¡Cómo nos divertimos, ¿eh, Néstor?

¡Demonio de niño! ¡Ahí viene alguien que me libertará!

Le buscaba, Néstor. ¿Puede usted echarme una mano? Casi nada, sólo darme un empujoncito...

¡Hmmm...! ¡Hmmm...!

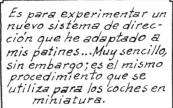

Es para experimentar un nuevo sistema de dirección que he adaptado a mis patines... Muy sencillo, sin embargo; es el mismo procedimiento que se utiliza para los coches en miniatura.

¡Hmm...! ¡Hum...!

¡Ah! Por ejemplo, en este momento mis ruedas están giradas hacia la derecha, y si me empujara ahora empezaría a dar vueltas sobre el mismo sitio.

¡Hmm...! ¡Hmm...!

Pero creo que, a pesar de su tristeza, el angelito mío será el rayo de sol que llena de vida, calor y alegría su vieja mansión.

Cierto, cierto.

Pero explíquenme cómo están ustedes aquí. Entren y siéntense. Seguramente estarán cansados y tendrán hambre y sed. Voy a hacerles servir algo.

Bien, Alteza, si estamos aquí es para intentar ayudarle y aclarar un asunto en el que el Arabair parece jugar un gran papel.

¿El Arabair? ¡Ah, perros! ¡Me pagarán caras sus traiciones! Yo les había autorizado para hacer en Wadesdah una escala importante en el camino de La Meca...

Un día, hace de esto tres meses, mi pequeño Abdallah, ese puro zafiro, sintió el deseo de ver a los aviones del Arabair haciendo algunos "loopings" antes de aterrizar en Wadesdah...

¿"Loopings"? Pero Alteza...

Una cosa bien sencilla, ¿verdad?, y eso le hubiese dado tal alegría a mi querido corderito... Pues bien, en vez de aprovechar esta ocasión y contentar a mi pastelito de miel, rehusaron con no sé qué malos pretextos.

Pero, Alteza...

Naturalmente que me enfadé y les amenacé con romper nuestro contrato. ¡Ah! Y aún les hice otra amenaza, la de revelar al mundo que el Arabair se dedica al tráfico de esclavos.

¿QUE?

GRRR

Sí, sí, al tráfico de esclavos, eso es. Los aviones que llegan de África y hacen escala en Wadesdah están llenos a rebosar de negros sudaneses y senegaleses que, convertidos al islamismo, van en peregrinación a La Meca.

Sí...¿Y qué...?

De regreso, por el contrario, sus aviones están casi vacíos. ¿Por qué? Pues porque en algún lugar entre Wadesdah y La Meca, esos negros son vendidos como esclavos...

¡Pero es una cosa espantosa!

Pues sí... Pero volviendo a lo del Arabair, esos chacales han fomentado el malestar en el país y gracias a su apoyo ha tomado el poder el infame Bab El Ehr...aunque no será por mucho tiempo, porque yo barreré a ese perro sarnoso, a esa hiena hedionda, a esa serpiente viscosa...

GROUW

¡Por Alá! Ojalá que su perro no se haya acercado a Aïcha.

GRROUW

? !

?

CRAC GROUW

¡Ahmed, de prisa! ¡Aïcha!

¡Ah! ¿conque usted también estaba aquí?

Sí, un guepardo amaestrado, pero ya ha visto lo que pasa cuando se le irrita... Es como yo: que tengan cuidado aquellos que me atacan... El pérfido Bab El Ehr lo sabrá algún día...

GRRR!...

... Y también este infame de Gorgonzola, propietario del Arabair.

¿El Arabair pertenece a Gorgonzola?

Al mismo. Armador, propietario de cadenas de periódicos, de radio y televisión, propietario de firmas cinematográficas, de líneas aéreas, mercader de perlas y de cañones, mercader de esclavos, Gorgonzola es el hombre que ha permitido a Bab El Ehr tomar el poder. Pero, paciencia, porque los bienes mal adquiridos nunca aprovechan.

¡Es una gran verdad eso!

Se debiera impedir que ese canalla internacional hiciera más daño.

Sí, claro, ¿pero cómo descubrir su odioso tráfico de esclavos?

Diga, Alteza, la estación término del Arabair es La Meca, ¿verdad? Bueno. ¿Hay algún medio de llegar allí ahora?

¡Je, je! Esto se pone interesante.

¿A La Meca? No es fácil, por el momento, pero dénme dos o tres días y hallaré el medio de embarcarles a bordo de un velero que les llevará.

Muy bien, Alteza

¡Je, je! Bab El Ehr se alegrará.

GROUW!

Bueno, ¿qué ha pasado?

Es Ben Youssef, señor... Aïcha se le ha echado encima... Vean, necesita por lo menos tres semanas para reponerse. Por lo visto ha pisado la cola a Aïcha.

¡Oh! ¡Pobre animal...!

Tres días más tarde...

Todo está arreglado. Saldrán mañana al amanecer con dos hombres de confianza que les guiarán hacia un lugar de la costa; allí les esperará un barquito que les llevará hasta La Meca... Pero estén prevenidos: Gorgonzola es un hombre peligroso.

Han pasado dos días...

Ya estamos, pueden desmontar... Pero esperen ahí, voy a ver si está realmente el barco.

Nos hace señales para que avancemos.

Ahí tienes el cascarón a bordo del que tenemos que embarcar. Es un butre. Me equivoco, es un "sambuk".

Acaban de echar una embarcación a la mar.

¡Alerta, alerta! Una patrulla de "meharistas"

¡Por las barbas del Profeta! Hay algo sospechoso allá abajo.

¡Alto! ¿Quién vive?

¡Por Alá, han tropezado con una patrulla!

¡Ja, ja, ja! ¿A eso le llaman soldados? Déjame que me ría... Al primer tiro al aire corren como conejos.

Al amanecer...

¡Ja, ja! ¡Ja, ja!

¡Ja, ja, ja...! Todavía me acuerdo del galope de esos paniaguados de guardacostas. Parecía que iban a traspasar la barrera del sonido.

Sí... Desgraciadamente habrán dado la alerta, y en ese caso...

¡Hay que ver lo pesimista que eres! ¿Qué temes? ¿Que manden una escuadra de acorazados por nosotros?

No, claro que no, pero...

¿Qué?

¡Mire allá, capitán! Allí está lo que yo me temía.

¡Truenos y rayos! "Mosquitos"

¡Den la vuelta...! ¡Van a atacarnos! ¡Cuerpo a tierra todo el mundo!

¡Bandidos! ¡Piratas! ¡Gangsters!

¡Si por lo menos tuviese un arma!

¡Y vuelven...!
¡Un arma! ¡Un arma! ¡Qué rabia!

¡A...a...aquí tiene!

¡Esta vez, él o nosotros!

¡Tocado!

¡Has dado en el blanco!

Y el otro avión huye. ¡Estamos salvados!

¡Capitán, capitán! ¿Qué ha ocurrido? ¡De prisa, vuelva en sí, que nos vamos a asar.

Mientras tanto...

¿Quiere usted concederme esta samba, princesa?"

Con mucho gusto, marqués.

¡Qué yate tan ideal para un crucero!

El "Shéhérazade" es verdaderamente un barco maravilloso y esta idea de dar un baile de trajes a bordo ha sido estupenda.

Perdón, señor marqués, le llaman por radio... Una llamada urgente...

Bien, ya voy.

¿Ve usted, mi querida amiga? Los negocios, siempre los negocios... Soy un esclavo... ¿Querrá usted perdonarme?

No faltaba más, marqués.

¡Qué delicioso anfitrión es el marqués! Este crucero a bordo del "Shéhérazade" es un encanto!

Sí, es un gran señor... Las malas lenguas aseguran que tiene un pasado más bien obscuro...

Es cierto que con tal exhibición de lujo no faltará la envidia. Hay que reconocer, sin embargo...

¿Oiga, oiga? K6WM a R3BO... Transmita en clave.

Fuertes picadas avispas a cabritilla azul. Parásitos 1 y 2 embotellados. Terminado.

K6 WM a R3BO... Comprendido. Terminado.

Bueno... ahora la clave y aclaremos esto... Los parásitos 1 y 2 ya sé lo que son.

Eso... ya entiendo... ¡Estupendo! Mull Pacha ha hecho un buen trabajo y hemos concluido con esos dos energúmenos.

Si esto continúa, capitán, pronto estaremos al régimen del doctor Bombard: plancton y agua de mar.

¿Yo...? ¿Beber agua de mar? Debes de estar mal de la cabeza, ¿verdad?

Pruébela, capitán, no es tan mala.

¡Ja, ja, ja! ¡Que no es mala! ¡Piensa en todos los peces que se pudren ahí dentro...! ¡Piensa en todos los ahogados que se cuecen a fuego lento ahí desde hace siglos...! ¡En las toneladas de detritos que los barcos arrojan todos los días... Eres libre de suicidarte bebiendo esta porquería, pero yo, "nanay".

Eso no muy bueno...

Además ...además...

Además... además.

YUPIIII

?

¡Allí...! ¡Un barco...! ¡Salvados!

Un barco... Y viene precisamente en el momento que acabas de tragarte este caldo de cultivos...¡Ja, ja, ja!

Un barco. Es verdad.

¡Ja, ja, ja! ¡Es para retorcerse de risa! ¡Ja, ja, ja!

¡Quiera Dios que nos vea!

!

PLUTCH

El, que no quería beber agua de mar... Pues va a quedar bien servido...

¿Por fin se ha decidido, capitán?

¿Yo...? Ni pensarlo, no he bebido ni una gota...¡glú!

¡Oh! El barco... él no vernos. él partir...

! ?

¡Truenos y rayos! Es cierto, se aleja... ¿Quién será el paleto de almirante que manda ese cascarón con una tripulación de marineros de agua dulce?

¿Qué hacer?...¿Qué hacer para llamar su atención?

¡Ah, una idea! ¿Tiene alguno de ustedes un espejo...?

¿Un espejo? ¿Para qué lo quieres?

Aquí... yo espejo...

¿Quiere peine también?

Bravo, pequeño, no se me había ocurrido.

No, gracias, solamente el espejo.

Anda, ¡mil rayos!, mándales el sol a la cara; tendrán que vernos por fuerza.

Es nuestro último recurso.

Señales luminosas a estribor, comandante.

Allá, comandante, ¿lo ve?

Sí, veo una balsa con tres hombres.

¿Diga? Sí, comandante, le escucho...¿Cómo? ¿Una balsa con tres náufragos? ¡Caramba! Espere, voy a verlos. Ni una palabra a mis invitados! Ya voy.

Allá, señor marqués... Vea las señales que nos hacen. Son tres, con un perrito.

¡Maldición...! Son Tintín y el marino barbudo y un tercer ladrón... Pero, entonces, el mensaje que Mull Pachá acaba de enviarme...

¿Voy a poner rumbo hacia ellos?

¿Para qué? Son unos bromistas que atraviesan los mares sobre una cáscara de nuez... Ya sabe usted, esos tres ingleses de los que hablan todos los periódicos. No necesitan nada. Continúe su ruta.

Pero, señor marqués...

Le digo que siga. ¡Adónde iríamos a parar si tuviésemos que ocuparnos de todos los chiflados que se lanzan a la aventura sobre los océanos! ¡Continúe! ¡Y ni mencionarlo a los pasajeros. ¿Comprendido?

¡Marqués...!¡Eh... marqués...!

¿Dónde está marqués?

Aquí. ¿Qué pasa?

¡Náufragos, allí, sobre una balsa...!

Es cierto, marqués, verdaderos náufragos. Es divertidísimo.

Sí, sí,... lo sé... Yo... Precisamente acabo de darle órdenes al comandante para recogerlos.

¡Oh!¡Qué contenta estoy! ¡Ver náufragos de cerca ha sido siempre mi mayor ilusión!

¡Da media vuelta!

¡Salvados!

¡Por fin nos han visto!

¡Salvados! Viva Sevilla ¡y olé!

¿Quiere usted que esto sea la Balsa de la Medusa?

¡Diablo! ¿Qué puedo hacer? No quiero que me vean...

¿Diga? Sí, señor marqués... Que no se pronuncie su nombre delante de los náufragos. Bien, señor marqués.

Además quiero que esa gente se sustraiga a la curiosidad de mis invitados y que no tengan contacto alguno con ellos.

¡Rayos y centellas! ¡Qué maravilla de barco! Eso es un yate de millonario.

Esos imbéciles se creen salvados... ¡Je, je, je! Dejen que me ría...

¡Truenos y rayos! ¡Muchachos, qué yate! ¿A quién pertenece? ¡Oh! Pero... Caramba. ¿Se celebra el carnaval a bordo?

SHEHERAZADE

Casi, casi; hay un baile de disfraces... y toda esta gente, ¿saben?, son altezas, duquesas, artistas, celebridades, etc. etc...

Pero, "per la Madonna"! ¡No me equivoco: son Tintín y su amigo el patrón de pesca Bardock!

Voy a recibirlos. El Arte debe abrir sus brazos a los hijos de la Aventura.

En nombre del marqués de Gorgonzola, sean bienvenidos a bordo, "carissime mie"!

¡Sálvese quien pueda! ¡La Castafiore! ¿Qué hacemos? ¿Nos volvemos a la balsa?

¡Mi querido Tintín!

Encantada de volverle a ver, mi buen Karbock...ejem...Harrock

'm roll, señora Castafiole... ¡Harrock'n roll!

Lo siento, señora, pero tenemos órdenes del señor marqués. Esta pobre gente está rendida de cansancio. Además... el contagio, ¿comprende usted?

¡Que se ha figurado usted! ¡Yo no estoy enferma!

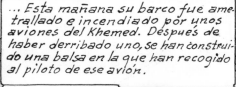
Un poco después...

Diga, Parker, ¿los ha interrogado?

Sí señor marqués. Iban en un "sambuk" que los conducía a la Meca...

... Esta mañana su barco fue ametrallado e incendiado por unos aviones del Khemed. Después de haber derribado uno, se han construido una balsa en la que han recogido al piloto de ese avión.

Está bien, Parker, gracias...

Perdone, señor marqués, pero tengo que hacerle notar que la señora Castafiore, que conoce a los náufragos, les ha dado la bienvenida en nombre del señor marqués...

¡Diablo!

¡El yate del marqués de Gorgonzola...! ¡Es inaudito! No salgo de mi asombro.

Oye, Tintín, ¿estás en la luna? ¡Di, Tintín!

No pueden quedarse a bordo. ¿Qué hacer? ¡Ah, ya sé! El "Ramona" está por estas latitudes... Es preciso que mañana nos crucemos con él como si fuese por casualidad.

Al día siguiente, de madrugada...

¡Vístanse, de prisa! Tienen ustedes suerte. Acabamos de cruzarnos con un mercante que se dirige precisamente a La Meca y acepta tomarles a bordo.

Ejem... Yo... Bueno... bien...

Unos minutos después...

Bien, asunto terminado. Y ahora, queridos amigos, les deseo una feliz travesía. ¡Ja, ja, ja!

¡Ah! Da gusto volver a pisar un buen viejo barco mercante.

Ahí tienen alojamiento ustedes dos. Su compañero irá a otra parte... Y el comandante vendrá a verles dentro de unos minutos y les traerá su "whisky".

¡Oiga, grumetillo, no tan aprisa! ¿Qué quiere usted decir con eso?

¡No hay derecho! Nos ha encerrado, ese especie de puerco espín mal hablado.

¡Abran! ¡Truenos y rayos! ¡Abran...! ¡Vaya maneras de salvajes...!

BOM   BOM

¿Qué hay, viejo borracho, ya empiezas a armar escándalo?

¡Allan...! (1)

(1) Ver "LOS CIGARROS DEL FARAON" y "EL CANGREJO DE LAS PINZAS DE ORO"

Estás contento de verme, ¿eh, viejo cachalote? Vamos a remojarlo con esto.

¡Allan! ¿Qué pasa, cómo es que...?

...¿Que estéis aquí...? Pues muy sencillo. Mando uno de los mercantes de Gorgonzola. Ayer recibí orden de cambiar de rumbo, y esta mañana, como por casualidad, nos cruzamos con el "Shéhérazade". No está mal el truco, ¿verdad?

Así es... ¿Y podemos saber lo que van a hacer con nosotros?

Si son buenecitos les desembarcaremos, pero no en La Meca, ¡claro! En Wadesdah.

¡En Wadesdah...! Pero si eso es la muerte... El sheik Bab El Ehr ha puesto precio a nuestra cabeza...

Eso, chiquito, no tengo yo por qué saberlo. Debes de tener sed; bebe a mi salud...

¡Ni pensarlo! Y vas a desembarcarnos en La Meca, ¿sabes?... Si no...

Si no, ¿qué? ¡Ja, ja, ja! Te aconsejo que seas buenecito. No olvides que estamos en el mar Rojo, donde abundan los tiburones. Ya lo sabes... Ahora, como soy buen chico, ahí te dejo esta botella para que te consueles.

Bye, Bye... Llegaremos pasado mañana. Así tendrás tiempo de pensar en un curioso problema: ¿duermes con la barba encima o debajo de las sábanas?

¡Ja, ja, ja! Muy gracioso lo de la barba.

No pegará ojo en toda la noche.

¿Encima...? No, así no va bien...

¿Debajo...? ¡Mil rayos! Tampoco va bien.

¡Cuidado! Quien bebió...

...beberá! Es verdad.

Vamos, sólo un traguito...

Pues sí. ¿Por qué no?

CLING

¡Encima...?

¿Debajo...?

¡Fuera la manta, ya hace demasiado calor!

Bueno... ahora ya está arreglado.

Y me voy a dormir por fin.

BANG BOM BANG BING
¡Por aquí, aprisa!
¡A las lanchas!
Ya está, ya estoy soñando.

¡Por aquí, Joe!
—BANG
¡Pero no, no son sueños...! Esos gritos, esas carreras, y las máquinas paradas... Todo es realidad.

¡De pie, ahora mismo!

?

¿Se ha caído de su litera?
¿Pues de dónde quieres que sea, del planeta Marte? ¡Levántate mil truenos! Tengo la impresión de que esta banda de ratones está huyendo del barco.

¡Abrid, truenos y rayos... !¡Abrid, o hago un disparate!
Intentemos derribar la puerta con esta cantina.

BOM BOM BOM

¡HUYYY!
¡Corramos, a ver lo que pasa!
C. OLSSON

!Corra, capitán, corra!

¡Truenos y rayos! Hay fuego a bordo...

¡Más nervio, muchachos! ¡Remad fuerte! Va a estallar de un momento a otro.

¡Naufragadores! ¡Piratas! ¡Filibusteros! ¡Sinvergüenzas! ¡Dejarnos plantados en un barco que se está hundiendo, ¡Qué el diablo os destripe!

Ven conmigo a popa, quizás encontremos una balsa.

Por lo visto tenemos vocación de náufragos.

¡EH, SOCORRO OH!

¡SIÑOR, SIÑOR!

¡Hombres en la bodega! ¡Qué raro!

¿Quién hay ahí abajo?

Nosotros buenos negros... Nosotros querer salir de aquí... Nosotros no poder respirar... Tener miedo...

¡Negros! Y parece que hay muchos. ¡Qué hacemos, capitán? No podemos abandonarlos, así.

Tienes razón. Ven.

Probaremos de sofocar el incendio... Sólo Dios sabe la carga que lleva este barco.

Dieciocho toneladas de explosivos y municiones. ¡Habrá bonitos fuegos artificiales!

¡Ya está! La manga está conectada... Abramos el grifo.

!

Blub... Yo... blub... Ya lo tengo, cap... blub...!

Gracias. Yo atacaré al fuego... Tú te vas a babor y pones otra manga en acción.

¡Dios mío! Ojalá podamos con él.

Bueno, ¿y la explosión? ¿Es para hoy o para...? Pero no veo ni llamas ni humo...

Ya está... Se apagó... Una ola grande que ha estado a punto de echarme por la borda...

¡Truenos y más truenos! El incendio está apagado. ¡Media vuelta, muchachos, regresemos!

¡Qué suerte! Ahora, esos pobres negros, capitán...

Tienes razón; pero primero...

... intentaré poner en marcha las máquinas. Tú sube al puente y ponte al timón.

Media hora después...

¡Por todos los diablos! El "Ramona" se aleja. Alguien ha puesto las máquinas otra vez en marcha.

¡Uf! No ha sido cosa fácil, pero ya está...

¡Magnífico, capitán! Y ahora, los negros:

Sí, pero hay algo más urgente que hacer; una llamada por radio.

! ¡OH!

¡Mire...!

¡Pst! ¿Muerto?

No, vive... Parece que vuelve en sí...

Mi buen Pst. Hable: ¿qué ha pasado?

¡Huid vosotros! ¡De prisa! ¡De prisa! Hay fuego... Muchas municiones en el barco... De prisa; si no, explosión.

¿Municiones? ¡Qué piratas! Por eso huían como ratones...

Tranquilícese, Pst, el incendio está apagado, ya no hay peligro. Pero, ¿qué le pasó?

Ellos despertarme para marchar con ellos... Sin vosotros... Yo no querer. Yo querer despertaros... y enviar un radio.

Entonces ellos enfadados... Roto la radio y luchado conmigo... Entonces yo "Knock-out"... ¿Ellos fuera?

Sí, nos han abandonado, esos iconoclastas. Estamos solos a bordo con una banda de negros que se encuentran en el fondo de la bodega.

Si quieren yo poder ayudar. Reparar la radio yo puedo, por ejemplo para un S.O.S.

¡Estupenda idea! Muy bien, hágalo. Yo me voy en seguida para asegurarme si de verdad ya no hay peligro.

Un poco más tarde...

Puedes estar tranquilo, grumetillo, el incendio está totalmente sofocado.

Ahora me ocuparé de esos negros. Primero sacarlos de su agujero.

¡Salvad pobre negro!

Yo enfermo. Yo morir.

¡Ya va! Voy con vosotros.

¡Eh, eh!... ¿Queréis soltarme? ¡SOCORRO! ¡TINTIN!...

?

¡Trogloditas! ¡Calabacines! ¡Descamisados! ¡Soltadme!

¡Atrás, visigodos! ¡Atrás, anacolutos!

¡Resista, capitán, que ya voy...!

¡Valor, ya llego!

Perdone, capitán, pero no se me ha ocurrido otra cosa mejor.

No te preocupes, ya empiezo a estar acostumbrado...

¡Especie de coloquintos de grasa de antracita...! ¡Conque os saco de vuestro calabozo y todo lo que se os ocurre para darme las gracias es atacarme por la espalda...

Tú no enfadar, siñor... Tú no gritar... Nosotros no saber tú buen blanco. Nosotros creer tú blanco malo que encierra pobres negros en tripa del barco... ¿Dónde estar blancos malos?

Bandidos malos blancos nos han abandonado, pero si vosotros ayudarme a mí, yo conducir vosotros donde vosotros querer ir. A La Meca vosotros querer ir ¿eh?

Sí, siñor, a La Meca. Nosotros buenos musulmanes. Nosotros ir peregrinación a la tumba del Profeta.

Muy bien, se os llevará a La Meca, a condición de que cada uno obedezca las órdenes que la daré. Y para empezar necesito hombres para las calderas.

Yo, siñor...

Yo...

Yo...

Yo, siñor...

Dos días han pasado...

Si mis cálculos son exactos, pronto divisaremos Djeddah, el puerto de La Meca.

Sí, estos pobres negros están llegando a su destino...

¡Estos pobres negros...! ¡Estos pobres negros...! ¿Estás convencido de que iban a ser vendidos como esclavos? Es ridículo.

Si el Emir dijo la verdad, me temo que ésa sea la suerte que les espera.

¡Vamos, vamos! Eso son novelas folletinescas. En nuestra época, la esclavitud no existe.

Dígame, capitán, ¿llevamos o no llevamos coque a bordo?

¿Coque? ¿Qué dices...?

¡Siñor, siñor! Tú venir ver... Barco venir hacia nosotros.

!

¡Mira, un "sambuk"...! Será el práctico del puerto de Djeddah... No, estamos lejos aún de la costa... ¿Será un pesquero?...

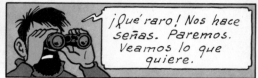

¡Qué raro! Nos hace señas. Paremos. Veamos lo que quiere.

El salam contigo, marinero... ¿Está arriba el capitán Allan?

¡El capitán Allan se acabó!... ¡Se fue! Ahora, el capitán soy yo.

¡Ah!, eres el suplente. Bien, bien... ¿El coque es bueno esta vez?

¿El coque? ¡Mil millones de naufragios! ¿Qué quiere usted decir con eso...? ¡Aquí no hay coque ninguno a bordo!

¿Que no hay coque a bordo?...¡Ja,ja,ja!

Ven aquí, tú.

Sí, sinor.

Sí... Buenos músculos... Bien... bien...

¿Y los dientes...? A ver, abre el pico, Coco... Ejem... No está del todo mal... Los dientes están sanos...

Oye, basta de bobadas. Este hombre no es un caballo ni un esclavo y...

¡Chissst! No debes nunca pronunciar esa palabra. Nosotros decimos "coque". Tú ya lo sabes.

¡¡Coque!! ¡Mil naufragios! ¡Tintín tenía razón! ¡¡Existen aún negreros!! Y éste es tu oficio, ¡bribón!...

¡Especie de traficante en carne humana! ¡Merecerías que te hiciera ahorcar en la verga del palo mayor!...

¡CUIDADO!

!

!

?

¡Especie de matón...! ¡Suerte tienes de que no te haga tragar tu barba!... Pero, largo de aquí, ¡víbora! ¡Que no te encuentre en mi camino!

¡Largo, filibustero!... ¡Fuera de mi vista, carne de horca!...

¡Sajú!... ¡Vendedor de alfombras!... ¡Paranoico!... ¡Imbécil!... ¡Caníbal!...

¡Ornitorrinco!... ¡Bebe-sin-sed!... ¡Bachibuzuc!... ¡Antropófago!... ¡Cercopiteco!... ¡Esquizofrénico!... Ejem... ¡Zopenco!...

No le oye, capitán, está demasiado lejos.

¡Ah! ¿tú crees?... ¡Pues todavía no ha terminado de oírme!

¿Adónde va? | Al puente.

¡PIRATA! ¡ECTOPLASMA! ¡COLOQUINTO! ¡RAPAZ!

¡FANTASMA! ¡OSTRÓGODO! ¡VÁNDALO!

Ahora sí que está fuera de su alcance...

¡Sí!... ¡Es una lástima!... ¡Negrero! ¡Eso es!

Pero, dime tú... ¿Cómo sospechaste de la palabra "coque"?

Ahora lo verá.

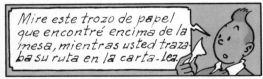

Mire este trozo de papel que encontré encima de la mesa, mientras usted trazaba su ruta en la carta. Lea.

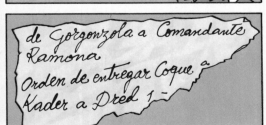

de Gorgonzola a Comandante Ramona Orden de entregar Coque a Kader a Dred 1—

¡Por las barbas del Profeta! ¡Este perro me las pagará!...

¡El fragmento de un telegrama enviado por Gorgonzola a ese bandido de Allan! Y "coque" es la palabra clave para designar su cargamento de futuros esclavos. ¡Qué bandidos!

Ahora hemos de hablar con esos negros. Han de comprender que ir a La Meca en tales condiciones es una locura.

Claro... Y también deberíamos intentar hacer una llamada por la radio.

¿Cómo va eso, Pst?

Todavía mucho trabajo, capitán.

Bueno, iré a hablar con los negros mientras tú pones rumbo hacia el sur; vamos a poner proa a Djibuti.

O.K.

Unos instantes después...

Amigos, escúchenme atentamente: ustedes emprendieron el viaje para ir en peregrinación a La Meca. ¿No es eso?

Sí.

Sí.

Luego pensaban, naturalmente, regresar a su país y reunirse con sus familiares. Es eso, ¿verdad?

Sí, sinor

Sí

Sí

¡Ay! Es otra la suerte que os espera. ¿Habéis visto a ese árabe que subió a bordo y a quien yo eché? Pues os espera en La Meca para venderos como esclavos. Como esclavos, ¿me entendéis bien?

Tú hablar bien, siñor. Malo, árabe, mucho malo. Pobres negros no querer ser esclavos. Pobres negros sólo querer ir a La Meca.

Claro, ya lo sé; pero os repito que si vais allí seréis vendidos como esclavos. ¿Es eso lo que queréis?

Nosotros no esclavos, siñor. Nosotros buenos musulmanes. Nosotros querer ir a La Meca.

Pero, ¡mil millones de mil naufragios!, me estoy matando repitiendo que si vais allí seréis vendidos como esclavos. Está claro, ¿sí o no? ¡Truenos y rayos!

Tú no gritar, siñor. Pobres negros querer ir a La Meca.

Bueno, especie de cabezas de mula, id pues a vuestra Meca. Pero os quedaréis allí para siempre. No volveréis a ver vuestro país de nacimiento. Nunca más ver familia. Siempre esclavos. Eso es lo que buscáis. Papanatas de zuavos, tontos de capirote...

Nosotros no zuavos, nosotros buenos negros, nosotros buenos musulmanes que querer ir a La Meca.

No hay nada que hacer... No tienen remedio; quieren ir a la Meca y se acabó. A romperse la cabeza contra el cabrestante.

¡Emyny sofoyy ooiboo-yi konychéere!

¡Yirò!

¡Beyni!

¡Loyotò!

?

Bueno, ¿qué queréis ahora? ¿Por qué esas discusiones?

Yo no querer ir a La Meca. Yo decirles: tú buen blanco, decir la verdad. Yo acordarme en poblado mío tres jóvenes marchar a La Meca dos años ya... No volver. Ellos esclavos, seguramente. Yo no querer ir a La Meca. Yo no querer ser esclavo.

¡Yo también no querer!

¡Yo también!

Bueno, muy bien. No he predicado en el desierto... Pues nos pondremos de acuerdo y los que no quieran ir a La Meca desembarcarán en otro puerto. Los demás pueden hacer lo que mejor les parezca.

Bien, siñor.

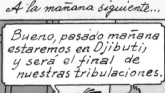

A la mañana siguiente...

Bueno, pasado mañana estaremos en Djibuti, y será el final de nuestras tribulaciones.

Si todo va bien, sí. Yo no estaré tranquilo hasta que hayamos llegado. Piense que Gorgonzola está al corriente de la situación y no ignora que nosotros sabemos... ¿Qué debe estar preparándonos?

RRRRRR

?

!

Un avión que revolotea sobre nosotros ¡Qué raro!

¿Oiga? ¿Oiga? "Albatros" a "Tiburón".. Localizado "Ramona" a 20 millas al oeste islas Farasan... Hace rumbo al sursudeste. Corto.

¿Oiga? ¿Oiga? "Tiburón" a "Albatros"!! Comprendido. Ponemos rumbo al oeste...

Se va... ¿Qué habrá venido a hacer?

No lo sé, pero no me gustan estas visitas.

Todo va bien. Mis hombres ya están sobre la pista. Dentro de unas horas, el "Ramona" habrá desaparecido con toda su gente. Así los testigos molestos estarán liquidados.

...para cruzarnos en su ruta... Punto.

¡Ya está! Mis órdenes han sido cumplidas.

Los manejos de ese avión me preocupan. Yo en su lugar cambiaría de rumbo, capitán.

Tienes razón, voy a hacerlo.

Unas horas después...

Bien, Pst, ¿ya marcha la radio? ¡No...!

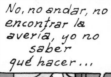

No, no andar, no encontrar la avería, yo no saber qué hacer...

RRRRR
¡Otra vez!

¿Será el mismo? ¡Cuidado con el cordón!

OH ?!

¡¡La radio!! Ahora, rota del todo, seguro.
! ?

¿Oiga...? "Albatros" a "Tiburón"... Encontrado "Ramona".

Gobierna todo al sur. Se encuentra a 30 millas al este de la isla de Dahlak-Kébir.

Me está poniendo nervioso ese pájaro de mal agüero.

¡Largo, moscardón, bandido, vete a volar a otro sitio y no en mi nariz, especie de animal!

"Tiburón" a "Albatros." "Ramona" a la vista. Preparamos la inmersión.

¡Dios mío! Lo siento de veras, Pst. Usted que llevaba trabajando tanto tiempo en esta radio... y yo estúpidamente...

¡Chut...!

¡Ya marcha! Funciona estupendamente ahora.

¿Qué? ¿Después de tal golpe? No puede ser, hombre.

Le digo que ya marcha... Escuche.

TUUT TUUT TUUT

¡Capitán, capitán...! La radio funciona.

¡Ay, perdón! Es que la radio, capitán, ya marcha.

¡Conque marcha la radio, ¿eh? Pues mire por dónde va...

... porque ya estoy harto de que me den en las narices. Hace un momento, un pez volador en medio de la cara, ¡plaf!, y ahora tú. Así que ¡basta ya!

¿Se ven peces voladores? Los miraré con los gemelos...

¡Qué bonitos son! Parecen pequeñas flechas de plata...

... surgiendo de las olas y que... Ahora salen dos... y allá otros tres...

Y allá... ¡Anda! ¿Qué es eso...?

¡CAPITÁN! ¡CAPITÁN! ¡UN PERISCOPIO!

¿Dónde está? Ya no lo veo, pero estoy seguro de que estaba.

Vamos, vamos, cálmate.

Allá, capitán, en esa dirección, estoy seguro... Allá a lo lejos... Que he visto su estela, le digo.

Ante todo, cálmate, grumetillo. Con periscopio o sin periscopio, calma...

¡Mil millones de truenos y rayos! ¡Un periscopio... allá, es cierto!

¡Alerta! ¡A las armas! S.O.S.... ¡La radio, Pst...! ¡Socorro! ¡En seguida! ¡Un submarino! ¡Zafarrancho de combate...! ¡Tengan serenidad y sangre fría! ¡Las mujeres y los niños, primero!

Calma, calma, capitán, que aún no está todo perdido. ¡Caramba!

Tienes razón, nada de pánico. Calma y serenidad.

¡La catástrofe! ¡Se acabó...! ¡¡Sin remedio...! Si son gentuza de Gorgonzola, estamos perdidos.

¿Y por qué?

Las municiones. En proa. Un torpedo ahí y... ¿te haces cargo de lo que pasaría?

Desde luego, pero ese torpedo todavía no está allí... ¡Vamos, rápido, cada uno, a su puesto!

Y no lejos de allí...

Casi los tenemos a nuestro alcance... Poco se imaginan lo que se les prepara...

Pronto estará la cosa solucionada... Tubo uno, ¿preparado?

Tintín a la radio. Usted, Pst, al timón. Repetirá mis órdenes. Cuidado; babor es a izquierda, estribor a derecha. ¿Entendido...?

S.O.S..... S.O.S.... Aquí s.s. "Ramona". Submarino desconocido en las cercanías. Tememos lo peor. Nuestra posición es...

Tubo uno, ¡disparen!

S.O.S.... S.O.S.... Aquí s.s. "Ramona". En peligro de ser torpedeados.

¡Torpedo a babor! Todo a estribor.

Todo a estribor.

¡Maldición! Han girado... Nos habrán visto...

S.O.S.... S.O.S...., Un torpedo casi nos ha rozado... S.O.S.... Daos prisa. S.O.S.

Un instante después, en el buque "Los Ángeles"...

Señor Comandante, un S.O.S. que acabo de captar.

¿Y qué historia negra de submarinos es ésta? ¿No se acabó la guerra?

Pero mientras tanto...

Timón 20° a estribor. Marcha, velocidad seis. Preparen tubo dos.

¡Hurra! Han captado nuestra llamada.

U.S.S."Los Angeles" a s.s."Ramona". Hemos recibido S.O.S. Vamos hacia vosotros. Estaremos ahí dentro de tres horas.

"Ramona" a "Los Angeles". Hemos podido evitar el primer torpedo, pero habremos naufragado probablemente antes de vuestra llegada.

Ahora está pasando a babor. Esta vez lo acertaremos, seguro.

Normalmente debe encontrarse por estribor. Dentro de un momento volveré a dar rumbo a babor para desconcertarle.

¡Barba a rabor! ¡Ay, no! ¡Barra a babor 30°!

Barra a babor 30°.

¡Por todos los diablos! Han girado otra vez.

Paciencia. Por fin tendrá que ponerse a estribor... Y en ese momento...

El submarino pertenece seguramente traficantes esclavos, jefe marqués de Gorgonzola a bordo motonave "Shéherazade", en crucero mar Rojo.

Barra a estribor 45°.

Barra a estribor 45°.

¡Ya está! ¡Lanzad el tubo dos!

Torpedo a estribor. ¡Truenos y rayos! ¡De prisa, al transmisor!

¡Adelante, mil truenos! ¡Full speed...!

¡Mil millones de mil naufragios!

¡Rayos y truenos! El transmisor de órdenes se ha encallado en "marcha atrás". ¡Rápido, un destornillador!

¡Maldición! Hacen marcha atrás... Nuestro torpedo va a pasar de largo otra vez. Son tenaces esos muchachos.

¡Hurra! Nos pasó por delante.

S.O.S. Por segunda vez un torpedo pasó a nuestro lado sin tocarnos. "Los Angeles", dense prisa.

Aprisa, a desencallar este dichoso mecanismo.

¡PCHKRAAPRVT!...¡TRRKHKRAAH...! Especie de endemoniado bazar de...

¡Qué asco de trasto...! ¡Toma!

¡AYYYYYY!

Continúan marcha atrás... Bien. ¿Preparados tubos tres y cuatro?

BING PANG

¡Toma, porquería de aparato tragaperras! ¡Toma!

?

¿Oiga...? ¡Oigan los de las máquinas...¡Oigan?

¿Diga, siñor?

BROOM

Demasiado tarde. Nos han dado.

¡BROOM!

¡Otra vez!

No, son cargas submarinas. ¡Uf! Creía que nos habían torpedeado.

Hidroaviones de la U.S. Navy, que han tomado por blanco al submarino. Seguramente son aviones del "Los Angeles"

¡Por mi abuelo! ¡Qué rociada! Si no quedan planos, como lenguados después de esto... ¡Ja, ja, ja, ja!

¡Espere! ¿Qué es ese remolino?

¡Mire! El submarino emerge.

Sí, les han sacudido de lo lindo.

¡Victoria! ¡Agitan bandera blanca! Se rinden. ¡E finita la commedia!

¡Oiga, oiga! Orden a submarino desconocido: quédese a la superficie y pare las máquinas. Al menor gesto sospechoso les lanzaremos granadas, esta vez al blanco.

Imposible tirar torpedos ahora... ¡Una mina bajo el casco! Con las municiones que llevan a bordo, pasará por un accidente... Ve, anda, tienes tiempo. La mina estallará dentro de una hora.

¡Corre, que vuelven!

¡Va!

¡Qué asco de oficio!

¡Salvados! ¡Yupi! ¡Salvados!

¡Hurra!

¡Tralala-laika!

Eso, baile folklórico hombres blancos.

Me han dicho delante, que es donde están las municiones.

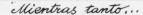

¡Mientras tanto...

Es muy bonito todo esto, pero tenemos que esperar al "Los Angeles"... Voy a ver si hay modo de echar el ancla.

Veintidós brazas de fondo. Muy bien.

¡Muchachos, echad el ancla! Ochenta brazas de cadena.

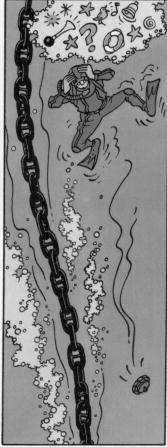

GLOB

HIP HIP HIP HIP HIP

Una hora después...

¡Hurra! Ya está aquí el "Los Angeles".

Crucero americano a la vista.

No os preocupéis, chicos. Va a estallar de un momento a otro.

HIP
BROOM

A la mañana siguiente...

Sin noticias de Kurt y de su submarino. ¿Qué estarán haciendo esos imbéciles?

...y militares que se incauten del m.s. "Shéhérazade" y prendan a su propietario el llamado Rastapopoulos, que se hace pasar por el marqués de Gorgonzola.

¡Perdido! ¡Estoy perdido! Pero no es posible...

RIIING RIIING

¿Diga...? Sí. ¿Que suba al puente? No tengo tiempo, comandante. Yo... ¿Qué? ¿Un barco de guerra? Ya voy.

El crucero "Los Angeles", señor marqués. Nos ha notificado por heliografía la orden de parar. ¿Qué debo hacer?

Repite el mensaje, Tom. Y añade que si no se para inmediatamente abriremos el fuego.

Está bien. Parad las máquinas y echad mi canoa particular al agua. Iré yo mismo a decirles a esos "cow-boys" lo que pienso de sus modales.

¡Ah! Ya obedecen... ¿Pero qué hacen ahora?

Parece que echan una canoa automóvil al agua... Y es Rastapopoulos quien se instala en ella...

No insistan, amigos, iré yo solo.

SHEHERAZADE

...Y viene hacia nosotros. ¡Hay que ver! ¡Qué descaro! ¡Atreverse a venir él, retándonos!

Pero ¿qué pasa? Aminora la marcha. Se ha parado. ¿Será una avería?

¡Dios mío, se hunde!

Ya está, les engañé. Prueben de pescarme ahora, señores, ¡Ja, ja, ja!

¡Dios mío! Es el profesor Tornasol. ¿Qué otra cosa habrá inventado?

¡Hola, profesor, vaya manera de darle a uno la bienvenida!

Pero... pero...¡qué estoy viendo? Bienvenidos a Moulinsart.

¿Para qué sirven los trastos esos?

Muy ingenioso, ¿verdad?

Patines con motor... Desde hace tiempo, yo intentaba resolver el problema de la circulación... Pensaba en un mecanismo ligero, manejable y reducido que...

¡Sí, eso es! Habrá que instalar luces rojas en las aceras, con su sistema a la grasa de cabrestante... Pero, oiga, otra cosa: ¿dónde está Abdallah?

No, un motor de dos tiempos de 28 cm³, con mandos de cable que permiten al mismo tiempo dirigir los patines y regular la marcha...

Es prodigioso, interesantísimo... Pero le estoy preguntando otra cosa: ¿dónde está Abdallah... Abdallah... ??¿DONDE ESTÁ ABDALLAH?

Bueno, aunque usted no lo crea: he alcanzado los 50 por hora... ¿Le gustaría probarlos?

¡¡Señor...!! ¡¡Qué contento estoy de volver a ver al señor !!

Hola, mi querido Néstor... Pero, mi pobre amigo, ¿qué le ha ocurrido?

Temo que la estancia del señor Abdallah no me ha hecho ningún bien... Pero ahora irá mejor. Se marchó ayer con todo su séquito. Dejó una nota para usted.

Pobre Néstor. Ese crío es un verdadero demonio. Vamos a ver lo que nos ha escrito.

¡Vaya! ¿No podría llamarme por mi nombre?

a mi querido Mil Rayos

"Mi querido Mil Rayos: Me he portado muy bien, no he hecho bromitas. Papá me ha escrito que debo regresar a casa. Lo siento porque me divierto en Moulinsart. Tu amigo Abdallah"

Es simpático, ¿eh? Néstor habrá exagerado preocupándose por inocentes niñerías...

¡Mil millares de mil millones de naufragios! ¡Otra barrabasada del niño! ¿Es que no me dejarán en paz nunca? ¡Mil truenos! En paz...

Señor, acaba de llegar el señor Latón...

¿Quién...? ¿Serafín Latón...? ¡Ah, no... no...! Quiero estar tranquilo...

Salud, hermanito, ¿cómo estás tú tan bonito? Yo estupendo, ya lo ves. ¡Ja, ja, ja, ja! ¡Qué gusto da volverse a ver! ¿Verdad mi viejo?

Ejem...

¡Ah, viejo barbudo! Te he preparado una sorpresa. Sí, porque el campo es muy bonito pero aburrido...

Eso depende del gusto...

No, no. Es aburrido, te lo aseguro. Entonces yo me dije "Serafín, hemos de distraer a ese viejo filibustero..."

Es usted muy amable, pero yo...

No hay pero que valga. Para mí, la cosa es fácil. Como soy el presidente de "Volante Club" de mi lugar, pues he organizado un "rallye" y la última etapa se corre...

¡...aquí, en tu casa!

FIN